STRUCTURED EXERCISES in STRESS MANAGEMENT

A WHOLE PERSON™ HANDBOOK
FOR TRAINERS, EDUCATORS AND GROUP LEADERS

VOLUME 3

edited by
Nancy Loving Tubesing, EdD
and
Donald A Tubesing, MDiv, PhD

Whole Person Press

Printed in the United States of America
by Port Cities Printing, Superior WI

10 9 8 7 6 5 4 3 2

Published by: WHOLE PERSON PRESS
1702 E Jefferson St
PO Box 3151
Duluth MN 55803
218/728-6807

PREFACE

*Three years ago we launched an experiment in health education --
the Whole Person HANDBOOK series of Structured Exercises in
Stress Management and Wellness Promotion. We believed then that
the time had come to move beyond peptalks and handouts to an
experiential approach that actively involves the participant --
as a whole person -- in the learning process.*

*The experiment has been an enormous success! The HANDBOOKS have
found their way into the libraries of trainers, consultants,
counselors, teachers, pastors, adult educators, nurses, managers,
group workers, health educators, chaplains, psychologists and
physicians around the world. We're proud that these Volumes have
been a catalyst for dramatic changes in health education.*

*Volumes 3 of the Whole Person HANDBOOKS in Stress and Wellness
carry on the tradition of excellence started by their predeces-
sors. Each HANDBOOK contains 36 all new structured exercises,
complete with step-by-step instructions for easy use. Some
utilize new applications of familiar group processes and techniques. Others were submitted by people like you who continually
strive to add the creative touch in their teaching. All have
been field-tested with a variety of audiences.*

*Please note our policy for reproduction of the HANDBOOK contents.
Our purpose in publishing these Volumes is to foster interprofes-
sional networking and to provide a framework through which we can
all share our most effective ideas with each other. The layout
is designed for easy photocopying of worksheets and training
notes.*

*Feel free to adapt and duplicate any sections of the HANDBOOK for
your use in training or educational events -- as long as you use
the proper citation as indicated on the facing page. However,
all materials are still protected by copyright. Prior written
permission from Whole Person Press is required if you plan large-
scale reproduction or distribution of any portion of the HAND-
BOOK. If you wish to include any material in another publication
for sale, please send us your request and proposal.*

*We are grateful to the many creative trainers who have so gener-
ously shared their "best" with you in these HANDBOOKS. Why not
return the favor? We encourage you to submit your favorite
structured exercises for inclusion in future Volumes. You'll
find instructions in the FUTURE CONTRIBUTORS section on page 138.
Do let us know what works well for you so that we can carry on
the tradition of providing a forum for the exchange of innovative
teaching designs.*

Duluth MN　　　　　　　　　　　　　　*Nancy Loving Tubesing*
February 1986　　　　　　　　　　　　*Donald A Tubesing*

WHOLE PERSON ASSOCIATES INC
consultants and publishers

specialists in stress and wellness programs with a whole person focus

CONSULTATION
+ development and implementation of stress management and wellness programs for clients around the world
+ curriculum design
+ creative problem solving
+ interdisciplinary think tank

CONTINUING EDUCATION
+ workshops, inservice training, keynote speeches, conferences on stress, burnout, wellness, self-care, vitality, communication
+ for professional organizations, community-based helping agencies, hospitals, business, government, education, civic groups

PRODUCT DEVELOPMENT
+ research and development of wellness-oriented products for health-conscious businesses and institutions
+ design of creative stress management premiums and promotions for employees, clients, customers

PUBLISHING
+ Stress and Wellness Handbook series for trainers, educators and group leaders
+ innovative training materials, tape and workbook packages
+ unique "workshop-in-a-book" self-help guides
+ practical "workshop-in-a-box" cassette tape programs
+ unusual relaxation tapes
+ health-related educational games

TABLE OF CONTENTS

ICEBREAKERS

73 INTRODUCTIONS VI 1
    Models
    Under Fire

74 AGENDA CONSENSUS 4

75 MARAUDERS 6

76 PANDORA'S BOX 10

77 TRAVELING TRIOS 12

78 GOING TO JERUSALEM 14

STRESS ASSESSMENTS

79 SPICE OR ARSENIC? 17

80 ON THE SPOT 21

81 DRAINERS AND ENERGIZERS 26

82 LIFETRAP III: SICK OF CHANGE 30

83 JOB DESCRIPTIONS 40

84 THE LAST CHRISTMAS TREE 44

MANAGEMENT STRATEGIES

85 METAPHORS 49

86 S.O.S. FOR STRESS 54

87 STRESS CLUSTERS 59

88 CORPORATE PRESENTATION 66

89 IMAGINE SUCCESS 68

SKILL BUILDERS

90 CONFLICT MANAGEMENT 73

91 EIGHT MINUTE STRESS BREAK 80

92 STOP LOOK AND LISTEN 84

93 CENTERING MEDITATION 92

ACTION PLANNING/CLOSURE

94 CLOSING FORMATION 97

95 EXIT INTERVIEW 100

96 RECIPE FOR SUCCESS WITH STRESS 104

97 MY STRESS REDUCTION PROGRAM 107

98 CHANGE PENTAGON 110

GROUP ENERGIZERS

99   KICKING YOUR STRESS HABITS CAN-CAN 113

100 CHINESE SWING 114

101 CLOUDS TO SUNSHINE 116

102 DO-IT-YOURSELF SINGALONG 118

103 GROANS AND MOANS 120

104 TUG OF WAR 122

105 WARM HANDS 124

106 WHAT'S THE HURRY? 126

107 YOU'RE NOT LISTENING! 129

108 PUSHING MY BUTTONS 131

CONTRIBUTORS
. . . . 134

WHOLE PERSON PUBLICATIONS
. 139

INTRODUCTION

Stress is a fact of life -- and from the board room to the emergency room to the living room people are searching for ways to manage stress more positively.

Structured Exercises in Stress Management Volume 3 provides 36 designs you can use for helping people move beyond information to implementation. Each exercise is structured to creatively involve people in the learning process, whatever the setting and time constraints, whatever the sophistication of the audience. To aid you in the selection of appropriate content and process to meet your objectives, the exercises are grouped into six broad categories:

Icebreakers: These seven short (10-20 minutes) and lively exercises are designed to introduce people to each other and to the subject of stress management. Try combining an ice-breaker with an exercise from the assessment or management section for an instant evening program.

Stress Assessments: These exercises explore the symptoms, sources and dynamics of stress. All six processes help people examine the impact of stress in their lives. You'll find a mixture of shorter assessments (30-60 minutes) and major theme developers (60-90 minutes). Any exercise can easily be contracted or expanded to fit your purpose.

Management Strategies: The five processes in this section focus on general strategies for dealing with the stress of life. Participants evaluate their coping patterns and explore new alternatives for managing stress.

Skill Builders: Each volume in the HANDBOOK series concentrates on a few coping skills in more depth. The four exercises in this section highlight conflict management, stretching, listening and meditation/relaxation.

Action Planning/Closure: These five exercises help participants draw together their insights and determine actions they wish to take on their own behalf.

Energizers: The ten energizers are designed to perk up the group whenever fatigue sets in. Sprinkle them throughout your program to illustrate skills or concepts. Try one for a change of pace -- everyone's juices (including yours!) will be flowing again in 5-10 minutes.

The HANDBOOK format is designed for easy use. You'll find that
each exercise is described completely, including:

- goals
- group size
- time frame
- materials needed
- step-by-step process instructions
- variations

*Special instructions for the trainer and scripts to be read to
the group are typed in italics.*
Questions to ask the group are preceded by a □.
Mini-lecture notes are preceded by a ● or a *.

Although the processes are primarily described for large group
(25-100 people) workshop settings, most of the exercises work
just as well with small groups, and many are appropriate for
individual therapy or personal reflection.

If you are teaching in the workshop or large group setting, we
believe that the use of small discussion groups is the most
potent learning structure available to you. We've found that
groups of four persons each provide ample "air time" and a good
variety of interaction. If possible, let groups meet together
two or three different times during the learning experience
before forming new groups.

These personal "sharing groups" allow people to make positive
contact with each other and encourage them to personalize their
experience in depth. On evaluations, some people will say "Drop
this," others will say, "Give us more small group time," but most
will report that the time you give them to share with each other
becomes the heart of the workshop.

If you are working with an intact group of 12 people or less, you
may want to keep the whole group together for process and
discussion time rather than divide into the suggested four or
six person groups.

Each trainer has personal strengths, biases, pet concepts and
processes. We expect and encourage you to expand and modify what
you find here to accommodate your style. Adjust the exercises as
you see fit. Bring these designs to life for your participants
by inserting your own content and examples into your teaching.
Experiment!

And when you come up with something new, let us know . . .

ICEBREAKERS

73 INTRODUCTIONS VI (p 1)

In these two quick icebreakers, participants introduce themselves by describing someone who handles stress well (MODELS) and explore their reactions to pressure (UNDER FIRE). (10-20 minutes)

74 AGENDA CONSENSUS (p 4)

Participants use notecards to record their own expectations for the meeting, then compare notes with others in the group and identify which personal goals will and won't be met. (15 minutes)

75 MARAUDERS (p 6)

This highly active and entertaining sensory awareness exercise demonstrates the physical symptoms of stress. Participants learn to recognize their own unique patterns of reaction to stress. (20-30 minutes)

76 PANDORA'S BOX (p 10)

Participants get acquainted as they identify major sources of stress and discover a surprise ending. (15-30 minutes)

77 TRAVELING TRIOS (p 12)

In this fast-paced icebreaker participants move from group to group, meeting with each other and describing their coping styles. (10-15 minutes)

78 GOING TO JERUSALEM (p 14)

Participants use stress symptoms to play an old-fashioned ice-breaker. (10-20 minutes)

73 INTRODUCTIONS VI

In these two quick icebreakers, participants introduce themselves by describing someone who handles stress well (MODELS) and explore their reactions to pressure (UNDER FIRE).

GOALS

1) To get acquainted.

2) To raise consciousness about topics to be covered during the session.

GROUP SIZE

Unlimited; some modifications may be necessary with very large or very small groups.

TIME FRAME

10-20 minutes

MATERIALS NEEDED

UNDER FIRE: Simple prizes (eg raisins, gold stars, biodots) for the winning quartet.

PROCESS

MODELS

1) The trainer invites participants to think about someone they know who handles stress well. This could be a co-worker, a friend, a family member, a public figure, even a TV character.

2) As soon as everyone has a stress "model" in mind, the trainer instructs people to write down several qualities or attributes that make this special person such a good stress manager.

3) One by one participants introduce themselves to others in the group by describing in a few sentences the characteristics they would like to emulate in their model (eg, how they cope, attitude, level of stress).

4) The trainer may want to summarize the insights of the group and use them as a springboard for an in-depth presentation on successful coping styles.

UNDER FIRE

1) The trainer asks participants to find a partner and a private space in the room. Once everyone is settled, he asks the pairs to introduce themselves and take a few minutes to share one or two situations that they find particularly stressful.

2) The trainer calls time and invites each pair to find another pair and join in a foursome.

3) Once the small groups of four are settled, the trainer announces that the next ten minutes will be spent in an inter-group contest and describes the process in detail:

   * Each group will generate a list of stressors.

   * The youngest person in each group will be given a book of matches. She is to take a match, light it, hold it and name as many stressors as possible before the match burns out. Someone else in the group should keep track of the stressors named.

   * No additional stressors may be added after the match goes out. Only the person holding the match may contribute ideas to the list.

   * The next older person in the group will then light the next match and name as many different stressors as he can before the match goes out. Someone in the group should record all the new stressors, eliminating duplicates.

   * The process will be repeated until all have taken a turn. Each person gets only one opportunity.

   * A prize will be awarded to the group that comes up with the most stressors.

4) At a signal from the trainer, the groups begin.

5) As soon as all groups have finished, the trainer asks for a report on the total number of stressors named by each group and presents an appropriate small prize to the winning foursome (eg, sugarless gum, an empty bottle of "stresstabs", aloe leaves for burnt fingers, etc).

6) The trainer invites participants to reflect on the pressure they felt while completing this exercise -- and to spend 5 minutes in their foursomes sharing reactions to questions such as:

   □ What was the most stressful part of this exercise?

       ❑ What physical or emotional symptoms of stress did
         you experience?

       ❑ Do you experience similar symptoms when feeling
         hurried, on the spot or under pressure at work, at
         home or in social situations?

7) The trainer reconvenes the entire group and asks for
   comments about how people respond differently under
   pressure and for observations about the wide variety of
   symptoms they experience when under stress.

TRAINER'S NOTES

MODELS was submitted by Pat Miller.

UNDER FIRE was submitted by Mark Warner.

74 AGENDA CONSENSUS

Participants use notecards to record their own expectations for the meeting, then compare notes with others in the group and identify which personal goals will and won't be met.

GOALS

1) To identify and articulate personal goals.

2) To build group cohesion.

3) To clarify what will not be covered in the meeting.

GROUP SIZE

Works best with fewer than 30 people.

TIME FRAME

15 minutes

MATERIALS NEEDED

Several 3x5 index cards for each participant; blackboard or newsprint easel.

PROCESS

1) The trainer introduces the exercise, covering some or all of the following points:

- The subject of stress usually attracts people with all sorts of hopes and expectations.

- Often we are not consciously aware of the variety of goals we have for a learning experience and are vaguely disappointed when these unspoken agendas are not fulfilled.

- Usually we don't know if our needs are going to be met until the event has been completed.

2) The trainer explains that this exercise will allow everyone to have some input into what happens during the meeting and will also clarify which issues are outside the scope of this experience.

3) The trainer invites participants to consider their own goals and expectations as they begin this learning experience. As people are reflecting, he distributes

several 3x5 cards to everyone and asks them to write one goal on each card.

Note: While participants are writing goals, the trainer needs to make a consensus poster with two sections, one labelled "WILL BE MET PARTIALLY OR IN FULL" and the other labelled "WON'T BE MET -- NEED OTHER RESOURCES". Be sure to have plenty of tape for securing all the cards to the poster.

4) After most people have written their goals, the trainer collects all the cards, shuffles them thoroughly to insure anonymity and reads them one by one. As he reads each one, he comments on whether or not it will be met during the learning experience.

   * Agendas that will be covered <u>for sure</u> are posted in the WILL BE MET section.

   * Agendas that may be met <u>only partially</u> are noted, explained and posted in the WILL BE MET section.

   * Agendas that will <u>definitely not</u> be covered in the meeting are posted in the WON'T BE MET section. The trainer explains why they will not be met and gives suggestions for how these goals could be met elsewhere. Participants are also invited to write on these cards at break time, suggesting additional ways these goals could be met outside the session.

5) The trainer uses the WILL BE MET goal cards to highlight the agenda for the remainder of the meeting and to introduce the first topic.

VARIATIONS

■ After Step 3 participants could form trios, introduce themselves and share their goals and expectations. After 5-10 minutes the trainer asks each group to agree together on one goal they would all like to see accomplished during the meeting. These consensus goals are listed separately and incorporated into the trainer's agenda for the meeting.

TRAINER'S NOTES

Submitted by Jerry Glashagel.

© 1986 Whole Person Press   PO Box 3151   Duluth MN 55803

75 MARAUDERS

This highly active and entertaining sensory awareness exercise demonstrates the physical symptoms of stress. Participants learn to recognize their own unique patterns of reaction to stress.

GOALS

1) To identify the body's physical response to stressful events.

2) To demonstrate how stress is triggered by both positive and negative events.

3) To enable participants to recognize their own unique symptoms of stress.

GROUP SIZE

Unlimited, as long as space is large enough.

TIME FRAME

20-30 minutes

MATERIALS NEEDED

Blackboard or flipchart.

PROCESS

1) The trainer introduces the exercise by pointing out the following facts about stress:

- The stress response is a physical reaction -- the body's response to any demand for change.

- Although the mechanism is the same for everyone, each of us responds in a slightly different manner -- some with sweaty palms, some with tense muscles and some with hyperventilating or a variety of other symptoms.

- Recognition of these early warning signs can help you alleviate the physical impact of stress before it becomes too great.

2) The trainer asks participants to form small groups of six persons each. Five of the six people make a circle, facing each other with their eyes closed. The sixth

person remains outside the group and becomes the "marauder".

3) Round one. The sixth person (the marauder) is instruc- ted to slowly and silently circle the group. After prowling around the circle once or twice, the marauder stops behind the person of her choice and startles him by suddenly yelling "HA!" while grabbing him sharply at the waist.

The startled person then becomes the new marauder while the previous marauder joins the circle and closes her eyes, awaiting the next "attack".

The process continues for about five minutes or until everyone in the group has had a chance to become a marauder.

Throughout the exercise, the trainer gives continuous verbal guidelines to the circle groups, asking them to:

* *Notice any body sensations that you are experiencing while waiting for the marauder to strike (eg, tight shoulder muscles, clenched jaws, clenched fists, nervous stomach, shallow breathing);*

* *Refrain from judging these sensations -- ie, whether you like or dislike them -- instead get into the experience of them, focusing on just the sensations themselves;*

* *Pay particular attention to how you feel when you get "zapped" by a marauder -- notice the sudden "rush" you experience.*

Note: The trainer needs to repeat these guidelines several times (perhaps each time the marauder switches) in order to keep participants focused on their bodily sensations throughout the exercise.

After about five minutes the trainer calls a halt to the exercise, but asks people to remain in their groups.

4) Round two. The groups are instructed to repeat the exercise, except this time the marauder should replace the startle routine with a gentle and soothing massage of the neck and shoulders of his chosen "victim".

Again, the groups should continue to switch marauders until everyone has had at least one turn to give a massage.

Throughout this phase of the session the trainer offers
continuing verbal guidance by asking participants to
notice any anticipatory physical symptoms they may be
feeling while waiting for the marauder to select them.

* *Pay attention to your immediate reaction when first
  touched.*

* *Notice any subsequent physical sensations when your
  neck and shoulders are massaged.*

After five minutes the trainer again calls time, asking
the groups to stay put for further instructions.

5) Round three. The groups are invited to try the exercise
one last time, with a new set of rules. This time the
marauder is given a choice -- she may either startle
(grab) or soothe (massage) the person in the circle.
Again, the process continues as before with each new
marauder selecting a "victim" and choosing to soothe or
startle that person.

The trainer periodically directs participants to become
aware of whatever physical sensations they are
experiencing in anticipation of the marauder, using
prompts such as:

* *Whether you are startled or soothed, notice how you
  react when you are first touched.*

* *Pay attention to your physical responses after you
  have been touched.*

6) Processing the information. The trainer asks participants to describe the physical sensations they
experienced during the exercise and records their comments on the flipchart.

  □ How did you feel waiting for it to happen? Upset?
    Embarrassed? Foolish? Angry?
  □ Where did you notice areas of tension in your body?
  □ What other sensations did you experience?
  □ How did you feel about being touched?
  □ Was there any difference between anticipating shock
    versus pleasure?

7) The trainer helps participants generalize by asking them
to identify similarities between how they reacted during
the exercise and how they experience stress in daily
life. To facilitate discussion, the trainer poses one
or both of the following questions:

       ❑ Describe some of your typical stress reactions and what triggers them.

       ❑ What value is there in being able to recognize the physical signs of stress?

8) The trainer may want to close the experience by leading participants in a stretching or relaxation exercise to put the group at ease.

TRAINER'S NOTES

Submitted by Joseph J Giacalone.

76 PANDORA'S BOX

Participants get acquainted as they identify major sources of stress and discover a surprise ending.

GOALS

1) To identify personal stressors and promote self-awareness.

2) To promote group cohesion.

GROUP SIZE

Best with a group of 6-12 people; with larger audiences, divide into small groups for Steps 1-4.

TIME FRAME

Approximately 15 minutes. Discussion may last up to 30 minutes, depending on the depth and direction dictated by the needs/interests of participants.

MATERIALS NEEDED

A gift box (Pandora's Box!) lined with a paper on which is written the word "HOPE" (make the letters large enough to be seen by the whole group); small slips of paper (two or three for each participant); pencils.

PROCESS

1) The trainer distributes two or three paper slips to everyone. Participants are instructed to write one personal stressor on each slip of paper they have been given.

2) Participants put their stressors into Pandora's Box.

3) The trainer opens Pandora's Box, chooses a slip of paper, reads the stressor written there and invites participants to share their feelings and reactions to this stressor.

4) The trainer reads the remaining stressors one at a time and encourages discussion about the impact such experiences have in people's lives.

5) When all stressors have been identified and discussed, the trainer shows everyone that one thing remains in the box -- HOPE!

6) The trainer points out the importance of hope and posi-
    tive attitude in managing stress, noting that this
    learning experience is an opportunity for participants
    to open their own Pandora's Box and discover renewed
    hope for dealing with the distress they may find there.

    *Note: This exercise serves as a perfect springboard for
    an exploration of various means of coping with
    stress and distress.*

VARIATIONS

■ This exercise is also effective as an introduction to a
session designed to prevent or explore staff burnout issues.

TRAINER'S NOTES

Submitted by Marcia A Schnorr, RN, MS. Based on a group activity
designed by psychiatric nursing students.

77 TRAVELING TRIOS

In this fast-paced icebreaker participants move from group
to group, meeting each other and describing their coping
styles.

GOALS

1) To reflect on and affirm personal styles of managing
stress.

2) To make positive contact with many other participants.

GROUP SIZE

Works best with 16 or more people.

TIME FRAME

10-15 minutes

PROCESS

1) The trainer asks participants to stand and gather in
one area of the room. As soon as all are assembled,
people are instructed to find two other people whose
names have at least one letter in common with theirs.

*Note: If the participants don't divide evenly into
trios, make one or two groups of four rather than
a group of two.*

2) The trainer invites people to introduce themselves to
their two partners and share something about their style
of managing stress. She announces that the groups will
have 2 minutes for this initial introduction, so they
should make sure they learn something about each person
during that time.

3) After 2 minutes the trainer calls time (a harmonica or
whistle works well, especially in a large group). She
then asks the youngest person in each group to leave
and "cut in" on another group to form a new trio.

In this new group everyone again introduces himself and
briefly describes some other dimension of his coping
style. No repetition is allowed. The information must
be completely different from what he has shared with his
previous group(s).

4) After 2 minutes the trainer calls time again, asks the tallest person in each group to leave and find a new trio, and instructs them to describe still other aspects of their stress management styles.

5) Step 4 is repeated several times without participants repeating any information.

   Note: Use unusual, humorous criteria to determine which person leaves the group (eg, the straightest teeth, the biggest car, came from farthest away, shortest hair, longest fingers, etc).

6) When the group's energy begins to flag, the trainer instructs people to return to their seats and write a paragraph about their personal coping style as they described it during this exercise.

7) The trainer invites all who choose to read their paragraphs. She then moves into a more detailed presentation on strategies for coping with stress.

   Note: THE AAAbc's OF STRESS MANAGEMENT (Stress 1, p 49), COPING SKILLS ASSESSMENT (Stress 1, p 63), PILEUP COPERS (Stress 2, p 54), and SOS FOR STRESS (Stress 3, p 54) would be good follow-ups to this exercise.

TRAINER'S NOTES

78 GOING TO JERUSALEM

Participants use stress symptoms to play an old-fashioned icebreaker.

GOALS

1) To get acquainted.

2) To identify symptoms of stress.

GROUP SIZE

Up to 20. With more people, divide into groups of 8-16.

TIME FRAME

10-20 minutes

PROCESS

1) The trainer notes that this icebreaker will be familiar to most people and asks for a volunteer to explain the normal rules:

* One person begins by saying, "I'm going to Jerusalem and I'm taking an apple (or any other object that begins with the letter "a")."

* The next person repeats what the first person said and adds her own item, this time beginning with the letter "b" -- "I'm going to Jerusalem and I'm taking an apple and a balloon."

* The next in line recalls the previous items and adds something beginning with the letter "c".

* This process is repeated by each participant in turn until the group has covered the whole alphabet.

2) The trainer announces that for this game the airlines have limited the baggage that may be taken to Jerusalem and are instead requiring all passengers to name a symptom of stress before they board.

Note: If the group is unfamiliar with the concept of stress symptoms, you may want to stop here for a brief presentation on physical, emotional, inter-personal and spiritual symptoms. Elicit examples from the group and supplement them with ideas from the list below.

3) After the group is warmed up to the concept, the trainer invites people to play this modified version of Going to Jerusalem:

* Someone starts by introducing herself and the stress symptom (beginning with the letter "a") that she is taking to Jerusalem (eg, "I'm Sue and I'm anxious").

* The next person introduces himself, recalls the "a" stress symptom and adds a "b" symptom of his own (eg, "I'm Stuart and I'm anxious and bulemic").

* The process continues around the group until all have had a turn. If anyone gets stuck, the trainer should invite others to brainstorm stress symptoms beginning with that letter.

4) In conclusion, the trainer invites comments from the group on the variety of symptoms that may be related to stress.

VARIATIONS

■ Participants could name sources of stress or choose coping resources instead of listing symptoms.

TRAINER'S NOTES

STRESS SYMPTOMS

Anxiety, apprehension, addiction, arguments, apathy, abuse.
Boredom, back-biting, backache, blues, blahs.
Colds, canker sores, claustrophobia, compulsiveness, crying
    spells, cynicism, clamming up, conflict, confusion.
Drinking, drugs, depression, diarrhea, divorce, distrust,
    defensiveness.
Edginess, emptiness.
Fear, forgetfulness, flu, fatigue, frustration, flush.
Guilt, gas, grudges.
Hopelessness, heart attack, high blood pressure, headaches.
Indigestion, insomnia, irritability, irrational thoughts,
    indecision, intolerance.
Judgmental stance, joylessness, jitters.
Know-it-all attitude, knots in stomach or back.
Loneliness, lowered libido, lethargy, lashing out, lack of
    concentration.
Muscle twitches, martyrdom, mood swings.
Nagging, negative attitude, nightmares, nervousness, needing
    to prove something.
Orneryness, out of touch, out of control.
Panic, pounding heart, put downs, poor judgment, pushing too
    hard.
Quiet, quick to take offense, questioning.
Rudeness, rash, resentment, righteous indignation.
Sulking, stewing, spiritual void, self-recriminations.
Temper tantrums, too much to do, tension, trouble setting
    priorities.
Unhappiness, unforgiving spirit, uncertainty, unproductive
    approach to work, unrealistic expectations.
Volatile, vague aches & pains, values confusion.
Weight gain/loss, whirling mind, worrying, wasting time.
X-tra pounds, x-travagant living.
Yelling, yawns, yah buts.
Zillions of things undone, zero energy.

STRESS ASSESSMENTS

79 SPICE OR ARSENIC? (p 17)

Using an unusual measuring device, participants assess current and past stress levels and decide how much is enough for them. (20-30 minutes)

80 ON THE SPOT (p 21)

In this thought-provoking process participants examine situations in which they are most vulnerable to manipulations and, using **Ten Steps to Critical Thinking,** brainstorm ways to avoid being manipulated in the future. (30-60 minutes)

81 DRAINERS AND ENERGIZERS (p 26)

The checklists used in this exercise prompt participants to identify the negative stressors in their lives that drain them, as well as the positive energizers that refill them — at work, at home and at play. (10-25 minutes)

82 LIFETRAP III: SICK OF CHANGE (p 30)

In this multi-phase exercise participants examine the role of change in their lives and the stress it creates. The double assessment, both objective and subjective, allows them ample opportunity to explore their current risk level and to articulate with each other the nature of the changes they are experiencing. Finally, participants plan strategies for taking charge of their own level and pace of change as they move into the future. (60-90 minutes)

83 JOB DESCRIPTIONS (p 40)

Participants divide into separate male and female groups to examine how sex role stereotyping can lead to the interpersonal stress of conflicting expectations. (60 minutes)

84 THE LAST CHRISTMAS TREE (p 44)

This fantasy exercise enables participants to explore the stress associated with rejection. (20-30 minutes)

79 SPICE OR ARSENIC?

Using an unusual measuring device, participants assess current and past stress levels and decide how much is enough for them.

GOALS

1) To assess personal stress levels.

2) To explore individual variation in healthy stress levels.

GROUP SIZE

Unlimited

TIME FRAME

20-30 minutes

MATERIALS NEEDED

STRESS THERMOMETER worksheets for everyone.

PROCESS

1) The trainer begins with a general introduction to stress covering information such as:

- Stress is universal.

- Stress is not all bad. In fact, we need a certain amount of stress to be vibrant, lively, productive people.

- Too much stress can be disastrous. In large doses the "spice of life" can poison us.

- How much is too much? Healthful stress levels vary greatly from individual to individual. Your optimal stress level is different from others in your family or work setting -- or from others in this room! The key question is "What's the best level for you?".

2) The trainer distributes the STRESS THERMOMETER worksheets and asks people to list at the top of the page all the sources of stress in their life right now.

    Note: To prime the pump, solicit several examples from the group or list a variety of stressors.

© 1986 Whole Person Press PO Box 3151 Duluth MN 55803

3) The trainer invites participants to assess their
    present stress level, filling in the thermometer on the
    left to the level that seems to best represent their
    current life situation.

    When people have marked their current stress level, the
    trainer asks them to respond to the two additional
    questions at the bottom of the worksheet:
    □ Is this level spice or arsenic for you?
    □ Is your stress level stable, rising or falling?

4) The trainer announces that there is an imaginary stress
    thermometer running down the middle of the room, with "I
    QUIT" on one end, "ZZZZZ" on the other and the various
    levels spaced in between. Participants are instructed to
    stand up, take their worksheets and pencils along, and
    move to the place on this room-size thermometer that
    represents the personal stress level that they marked on
    their worksheet thermometer.

    *Note: You may want to prepare signs or placards to mark
          and identify the location of the different stress
          levels in the room.*

5) Once all have found their appropriate place, the trainer
    asks everyone experiencing the same stress level to form
    a group, introduce themselves and discuss what symptoms
    of stress are typical for them at this level.

    *Note: If some groups are too small, combine adjacent
          stress levels. If a group is too large (more than
          8 people), divide it into smaller units.*

6) Next the trainer asks participants to think back to one
    year ago, assess their stress level at that time, and
    mark it on the corresponding worksheet thermometer. As
    soon as people have done this, they are invited to move
    to the appropriate level on the room-size continuum.

    Once everyone is settled at their new location, the
    trainer asks for a show of hands in response to the
    following questions:
    □ How many people were at a higher stress level a year
      ago?
    □ How many were at a lower stress level?
    □ How many haven't changed in a year?

7) The trainer invites participants to place themselves on
    the thermometer one more time. They are instructed to
    reflect on the stress level they would like to be expe-
    riencing six months (or one month, or one year) from now
    -- and record their level on the appropriate worksheet
    thermometer.

The trainer invites people to move once again, relocating to the spot in the room that corresponds to their desired stress level.

The people at each stress level once again form small groups and discuss what steps they will need to take in order to reach (or maintain) this stress level.

8) The trainer reconvenes the whole group and asks for insights and observations.

Note: You may also wish to point out that a stress management course is not designed to eliminate stress -- thus producing a room full of "ZZZZs!" Rather, it is supposed to help each person move toward the level of stress that seems appropriate to that person. Therefore, if a course is to be successful, participants must keep their own personal goals in mind.

VARIATIONS

■ Participants could complete the Holmes "SOCIAL READJUSTMENT RATING SCALE" prior to Step 2. During Step 5 people in each small group compare notes on their Holmes scores. This activity provides a perfect opportunity to point out that the same amount of change may provoke different levels of stress in different people.

TRAINER'S NOTES

Adapted from DA Tubesing, Stress Skills (Duluth MN: Whole Person Associates, 1978).

STRESS THERMOMETER

My present stress:

My current stress level:

one year ago   goal

Stop the world — I QUIT!

Crisis

Close to the edge

Too high

A little more than I'd like

JUST RIGHT — Normal for me

Life a little dull

Too low

Ho-hum — ZZZZ

Is your current level of stress spice or arsenic?

Is your stress level stable, rising or falling?

80 ON THE SPOT

In this thought-provoking process participants examine
situations in which they are most vulnerable to manipulations and, using "Ten Steps to Critical Thinking," brainstorm ways to avoid being manipulated in the future.

GOALS

1) To increase awareness of the stress of manipulation.

2) To apply critical thinking techniques as a stress
   management strategy in potentially manipulative
   situations.

GROUP SIZE

Unlimited

TIME FRAME

30-60 minutes

MATERIALS NEEDED

Paper and writing utensils; copies of the MANIPULATION
PATTERNS worksheet and the TEN STEPS TO CRITICAL THINKING
handout for everyone.

PROCESS

1) The trainer announces that this exercise will help
   participants assess their vulnerability to being manipulated by others and by situations. He introduces the
   concept of "mind control" and describes how such manipulation occurs, using the following notes as guidelines.

   - Mind control is a form of social influence that is
     both stressful and unethical, since it restricts
     freedom of choice by manipulating people to act in
     ways they did not intend.

   - Usually when we think of mind control, we think of
     brainwashing or shock treatments or hypnosis --
     traumas which most of us, fortunately, never
     experience. Unfortunately, mind control is a much
     more common experience. We all experience it every
     day -- in all kinds of situations -- when we are
     consciously or unconsciously manipulated into doing
     or saying something we really didn't choose freely.

● Such manipulation is fostered by three major forces:
  <u>Situations and roles</u> that "demand" a certain behavior. All of us respond to <u>demand characteristics</u>
  in situations and relationships -- often without
  questioning, or even noticing. For example,
        Guests . . . don't complain;
        Big boys . . . don't cry;
        Team players . . . cooperate;
        Interviewees . . . answer questions;
        Children . . . do as they are told;
        Men . . . protect women;
        Women . . . are "ladylike".
  These and hundreds of other expectations that people
  "should act" in a certain way control our behavior
  and limit our choices.

● <u>Other people</u> who want us to do something. They beg,
  threaten, pout, cajole, sweet talk, push, lay on
  guilt, get mad or sad -- and adopt hundreds of other
  "clever" postures designed to get us to do what <u>they</u>
  want rather than what <u>we</u> want.

● <u>Our own mind games.</u> We set ourselves up for being
  controlled by our expectations, by what we tell
  ourselves, by what we believe, by our sense of
  morality and responsibility, by our knowledge of our
  shortcomings and mistakes, etc. Self-talk such as,
  "I must please everyone," "I don't deserve much," "I
  really should have done _____," "I need to be
  perfect," "I'm really very weak," etc, makes us
  particularly vulnerable to manipulation by others.

● Most of us develop personal patterns of vulnerability to specific types of manipulation. We can
  easily see through and resist some mind control
  forces, while repeatedly falling easy prey to other
  manipulations that "push our buttons!"

● Whatever the reason you lose or let go of control,
  <u>you</u> are the only one who can get it back -- only you
  can take control again.

2) The trainer distributes MANIPULATION PATTERNS worksheets
    to everyone and guides participants through the
    reflection process, one section at a time.

    *Note: For each section, read the question at the left
           out loud, give an example or two, then allow a
           minute for participants to write their examples.
           Then pose the corresponding "hooker" questions,
           give an example or two and wait a moment for
           people to write their responses.*

> *After repeating this process for the four manipu-*
> *lation questions, encourage participants to*
> *summarize their insights and uncover their*
> *personal vulnerability themes using the prompts in*
> *the boxes at the bottom of the worksheet.*

3) The trainer asks participants to form groups of three, getting together with people they know least well. Participants take turns sharing their stories and "most vulnerable characteristics" with the others. Each person describes situations when they were manipulated, giving details about why and how it happened. (10 minutes)

4) After each person has shared, the groups of three list on newsprint the most troublesome situations that "push their buttons," and the personality characteristics that make them most vulnerable to manipulation. They then brainstorm a corresponding list of clever ways each situation could be handled more efficiently so that the manipulation is avoided. The trainer notes that many suggestions may be humorous -- and that such out-of-the-ordinary approaches are often the most helpful.

5) The trainer reconvenes the large group and invites participants to share examples of their vulnerability as well as some of the best ideas they came up with for taking control of their actions and thwarting the manipulations they experience.

> *Note: People may need a gentle reminder to share only*
> *their own stories and not comment on those of*
> *others.*
>
> *Model the sharing process by giving an example of*
> *your own -- or adapt this one:*
>
> *I am easily made to feel guilty. If I see someone*
> *I have not called or written to in a year, I try*
> *to avoid them. Then if they say, "How come you*
> *haven't called . . . ?" I feel guilty. One*
> *solution is to practice first saying to them, "Why*
> *haven't you called?" They will handle the guilt*
> *much better than I will, I reason.*
>
> *After I've practiced that for a while, I will*
> *graduate to being able to hear "Why haven't you*
> *called?" without the guilt which leaves me open to*
> *manipulation, and I'll be able to answer, "Yes,*
> *we've both been so busy we haven't been able to*
> *get together!" Now it's not a game of who can be*
> *first, but the responsibility is shared.*

6) As people share their examples, the trainer comments briefly and points out how each alternative solution illustrates one of the TEN STEPS TO CRITICAL THINKING which he outlines on the board as the ideas arise:

1) Recognize demand characteristics. Rethink the expectations which seem implicit in situations and relationships. Is it necessary that experts are always sure of themselves? Should soldiers always follow orders? Must dinner invitations always be reciprocated in kind? You don't always have to do what's expected!

2) Remember, you <u>can</u> say <u>no</u>!

3) Recognize false dilemmas. Always add "none of the above" to any multiple choice!

4) Sleep on it! Recognize pressure to decide quickly. Don't act under stress.

5) Look for the hidden agenda. What is really being said? What is <u>not</u> being said? To whom, by whom and why is it <u>being</u> said?

6) Recognize logical fallacies. Be especially cautious of an "appeal" to your "sense of logic."

7) Know who you're dealing with. Ask blunt questions and don't accept vague answers. Find out what a person represents.

8) Recognize flattery.

9) Ask questions. Challenge authority claims.

10) Retain your self worth. Whatever happens, say "I'm great!" Don't be afraid to be different.

4) After several people have shared their stories, the trainer concludes by summarizing strategies for avoiding the subtle, everyday pressures of mind control and coping with the stress of vulnerability.

Submitted by Bob Fellows.

MANIPULATION PATTERNS
how I set myself up to be taken advantage of

When have you been convinced to buy something you didn't really want? Jot down one or two examples.	What hooked you? What feelings set you up to be manipulated?
When have you accepted a drink, drug (or even some food) when you didn't really want it? Jot down some examples.	What hooked you? What about you contributed to your action?
When have you felt manipulated or "taken advantage of?" Remember several instances and jot down a note about each.	How did you set yourself up to be taken advantage of?
When have you verbally agreed to something that you didn't believe was true? Recall one or two instances.	Why didn't you speak your mind?

SUMMARY THEMES: Look over your examples for insights.

What would you say generally "pushes your buttons" and gets you to do something you did not want to do?	What is your most vulnerable characteristic that sets you up to be manipulated?	If a member of this group wanted to take advantage of you, how could they best do it?

81 DRAINERS AND ENERGIZERS

The checklists used in this exercise prompt participants to identify the negative stressors in their lives that drain them, as well as the positive energizers that refill them -- at work, at home and at play.

GOALS

1) To identify the daily drainers that deplete energy.

2) To recognize and utilize the daily energizers that restore vitality.

GROUP SIZE

Unlimited; the group brainstorming in Step 2 is best done with 20-80 people.

TIME FRAME

10-25 minutes

MATERIALS NEEDED

One copy of DAILY DRAINERS and PERSONAL ENERGIZERS work-sheets for each participant.

PROCESS

1) The trainer instructs participants to fill in the boxes of the DAILY DRAINERS worksheet. (4-5 minutes)

   Note: Participants are to list all the minor stressful irritants that occur to them. It is not neces-sary, however, that they fill in each box. Two or three items for some categories, while other cate-gories may be left empty.

2) The trainer highlights one category at a time and soli-cits from the group 3 or 4 examples for each type of drainer. Participants are encouraged to expand their personal list by adding those suggestions of others that particularly apply to them.

3) Participants look over their lists and note the settings in which most of their stress-producing drainers occur (home, work or play).

4) Steps 1, 2 and 3 are repeated using the PERSONAL ENERGIZERS worksheet.

5) Again participants consider the list of energizers and notice how and where they get revitalized. The trainer encourages people to compare their two lists and reflect on the balance of drainers and energizers in the different contexts, recording their insights on the back of one of the worksheets.

6) The trainer solicits observations, reactions and insights from the group.

7) In closing the trainer points out that one way to decrease the risk of stress exhaustion is to increase the daily dose of revitalizing energizers. She then invites participants to identify one energizer they want to utilize more frequently in each life context -- at home, at work and at play.

VARIATIONS

■ If time is short, either the DRAINERS or the ENERGIZERS worksheet can be used alone.

■ For use as an icebreaker, the trainer chooses a specific box (eg something that annoys you where you work) and asks participants to pair up, introduce themselves and share the items they wrote in that space. After a moment or two, people are instructed to find a new partner, exchange names and share their responses to a different item from the drainer or energizer worksheet, as designated by the trainer. This process is repeated several times, each time with a new partner and a different answer box.

■ After Step 5 participants could form small groups and discuss their reactions to the worksheets, sharing their insights about the most surprising responses or general themes that emerged.

TRAINER'S NOTES

Excerpted from Tubesing, Sippel and Tubesing, Personal Recharging: Rx for Burnout in the Workplace (Duluth MN: Whole Person Press, 1981).

PERSONAL DRAINERS

Visualize the way you usually spend your day. Then list the **draining** aspects of your day — those places/activities/people/conditions that diminish your energy:

Activities/conditions/places/people that . . .	AT HOME	AT WORK	AT PLAY
ANNOY YOU			
ANGER YOU			
DISTRACT YOU			
DEPRESS YOU			
WORRY YOU			
WEAR YOU OUT			
BORE YOU			
FRUSTRATE YOU			
PLAGUE YOU			

PERSONAL FILLERS

Visualize the way you usually spend your day. Then list the vitalizing aspects of your day — those people/places/activities/conditions that renew your energy and well-being:

Activities/conditions/ places/people that . . .	AT HOME	AT WORK	AT PLAY
EXCITE YOU			
CALM YOU			
FREE YOU			
BRING YOU JOY			
SUPPORT/ NURTURE YOU			
STIMULATE/ CHALLENGE YOU			
GIVE YOU MEANING			
MAKE YOU LAUGH			
ENERGIZE YOU			

82 LIFE TRAP III: SICK OF CHANGE

In this multi-phase exercise participants examine the role
of change in their lives and the stress it creates. The
double assessment, both objective and subjective, allows
them ample opportunity to explore their current risk level
and to articulate with each other the nature of the changes
they are experiencing. Finally, participants plan strategies for taking charge of their own level and pace of change
as they move into the future.

GOALS

1) To understand the connection between stress, life
    changes and health.

2) To assess the levels and types of change present in
    current life situations.

3) To explore strategies for managing the stress of change.

GROUP SIZE

Unlimited

TIME FRAME

60-90 minutes

MATERIALS NEEDED

Blank paper; one copy of the CHANGE CHECKLIST and CHANGES
AND PERSONAL OUTLOOK worksheets for each participant.

PROCESS

Note: This is a five-part exercise:
> *A) 1-2-3 Change -- warm-up chalktalk with sharing in*
>   *pairs. (10-15 minutes)*
> *B) The Change Factor -- chalktalk on change, stress*
>   *and illness. (10-15 minutes)*
> *C) Exploring the Meaning of Change -- subjective*
>   *assessment. (10 minutes)*
> *D) Small Group Sharing (15-25 minutes)*
> *E) Taking Charge of Change -- wrap-up exploring*
>   *strategies for coping with change and personal*
>   *planning for anticipated change.*

A) 1-2-3 Change: Introductory Warm-Up (10-15 minutes)

Note: At the beginning of this session you may want to play
music that reflects the theme of change and sets the
mood for this exercise (eg, "Everything Changes",
"Turn, Turn", etc)

1) The trainer introduces the subject of change and the
    process of the session:

    ● Change is a part of life -- there is no escaping it!
      And since change always requires us to adapt, it
      always causes stress.

    ● Change can provide the spice of life. Without the
      stimulation of change -- new challenges, new
      experiences, new relationships -- life would be
      rather dull. Who would refuse a promotion or avoid
      a marriage or not have children just because it
      might be stressful?

    ● On the other hand, research shows that too much
      change can drain our coping reserves -- and it can
      make us sick!

    ● This session will help you explore change both from
      an objective and from a subjective, personal view,
      as you seek to discover the kind and amount of
      change that works best for you.

2) The trainer distributes blank paper to participants and
    asks them to reflect on the following questions:

    Note: Read the questions one at a time, giving a wide
          range of examples to stimulate reflection. Allow
          ample time for participants to answer each
          question before moving on to the next.

    ☐ Think about all the changes that have occurred for
      you during the past year. Please write down three
      things that you chose to change -- of your own free
      will (eg, career, living accommodations, work sche-
      dule, new car, redecorating, hair style, etc).

    ☐ Now make note of three changes that occurred to you,
      about which you had no choice, over which you had no
      control (eg, death, local grocery closed, trip
      cancelled because of weather, your injured back, a
      friend moved, etc).

    ☐ Next list three changes you would like to make in
      the future (eg, be less impatient, write more
      letters, get a new job, retire, get married, save

© 1986 Whole Person Press PO Box 3151 Duluth MN 55803

more money, volunteer somewhere, etc).

- ☐ Please look over your list of nine changes and note which was (or would be) most difficult for you.
- ☐ Which change was (or is) most desirable?
- ☐ Which one caused you (or probably will cause you) the most stress?

3) The trainer directs participants to pair up with a neighbor and share some of the experiences and responses that were elicited by these questions. (5 minutes)

4) After the total group has been reconvened people are invited to share a few observations and insights on the nature of change in their lives and their varied reactions to it.

B) The Change Factor: Objective Assessment (10-15 minutes)

Note: The concepts and worksheet in this section are based on the research of Holmes and Rahe at the University of Washington. Their "Social Readjustment Rating Scale" could be substituted for the worksheet here.

5) The trainer expands on the relationship between stress and change, covering some or all of the following points:

- Endocrinologist Hans Selye coined the word stress to describe a phenomenon he observed and studied in his research. He defined stress as, "The non-specific response of the body to any demand placed on it."

- From this definition we can conclude that life is inherently stressful because it is full of change. Any change requires adaptation and therefore puts demands on our body systems.

- Every year all of us experience a wide variety of life changes -- both predictable events like a child going away to college, as well as unexpected occurrences such as a job layoff or winning the lottery!

- While some of these changes may seem positive or desirable and others negative, research indicates that they are all stressful!

6) The trainer distributes the CHANGE CHECKLIST worksheet to participants and guides them through the process of filling it out. People first mark each life event they

have experienced <u>during the past year</u>. (If the event
has happened more than once, they should indicate the
number of times.)

When nearly everyone is finished the trainer instructs
people to read through the list again, marking with a
star (*) those life events that were <u>particularly</u>
<u>stressful</u> to them -- and then answer the questions at
the bottom of the worksheet.

As people are finishing up, the trainer polls the group,
asking for a show of hands in response to the following
additional questions:

- □ How many experienced none of the listed life events
  this past year?
- □ How many experienced 5 or less?
- □ How many 10 or more?
- □ How many 15 or more?

7) The trainer summarizes research findings on the
    relationship between change, stress and sickness,
    covering some or all of the points below.

    ● Whatever the source, change is stressful by its very
      nature. When too many changes occur too fast, we
      put excessive strain on our system. As we struggle
      to adapt we may feel depressed, get physically sick
      or make foolish decisions.

    ● Research into the relationships between life change,
      stress and health supports the common sense notion
      that change takes its toll. Studies at the
      University of Washington have demonstrated four
      attributes of change.

    ● Some changes consistently cause more stress than
      others. The death of a young child is more stress-
      ful than a financial reversal, a divorce more
      stressful than a job change.

    ● Both positive and negative changes are stressful.
      Both call for system-wide adaptation. A promotion
      can be just as stressful as a demotion.

    ● Changes tend to come in clusters, creating their
      own momentum. One change leads to another. The
      stress also escalates, of course, as one adaptation
      demands another.

    ● An accumulation of changes over time, or a large
      number of changes in a brief period, increases
      stress -- and the risk of physical illness.

C) Exploring the Meaning of Change: Subjective Assessment
   (10 minutes)

   8) The trainer distributes CHANGES AND PERSONAL OUTLOOK
       worksheets to everyone and guides them through the
       reflection and writing process, giving several examples
       at each step.

       He instructs participants to select (from the previous
       worksheet) one "high stress" change and one "low stress"
       change that has occurred recently. These changes should
       be written in the appropriate boxes at the top of the
       CHANGES AND PERSONAL OUTLOOK worksheet.

       Participants are directed to reflect on and record the
       multitude of adaptations and adjustments that were
       required as a result of that change. (2-3 minutes)

       The trainer next asks people to identify and list their
       perceptions of that change.

           □ How did you interpret the event?
           □ What meanings did you assign to it?
           □ What overall outlook did you use to view the event?
           □ What consequences did you imagine?

       Note: Encourage people to list all the extremes that
             occur to them.

       Finally, participants are invited to analyze and
       summarize the relationships they see between their
       interpretation of the event and the amount of stress it
       caused them. These observations are recorded on the
       bottom of the worksheet.

D) Small Group Sharing and Discussion (15-25 minutes)

   9) The trainer divides participants into groups of four
       people each, or invites them to rejoin small groups from
       earlier in the learning experience.

       He instructs participants to take five minutes each to
       ·share their summary of current life changes and the
       personal insights generated by the objective assessment
       (CHANGE CHECKLIST) and the subjective assessment (CHANGE
       AND PERSONAL OUTLOOK) activites.

       Note: Announce that each participant may use the time in
             any way she chooses and may share in whatever way
             seems appropriate to her. The emphasis should be
             on allowing everyone her full five minutes to

> *share and be heard.* *Encourage participants to*
> *listen as carefully as they can, and when their*
> *turn comes, to share as personally as they are*
> *willing.*

10) The trainer reconvenes the total group and asks for
general observations from participants before moving on.

E) Taking Charge of Change: Planning Strategies for Coping
(15-25 minutes)

11) The trainer notes that change is both unavoidable and
desirable. But the stress of change can be minimized by
managing it effectively.

The trainer facilitates a discussion on change management strategies by asking the group for suggestions on
how best to manage change at home or on the job. As
salient points emerge, he writes them on newsprint or
the blackboard, asking for examples and amplifying the
discussion as necessary.

If the following ideas for taking charge of change do
not emerge during the course of the discussion, the
trainer may want to introject them in his closing
summary.

* Take good care of yourself. Build up your resis-
tance by practicing positive health habits such as
adequate rest, good nutrition, exercise, a regular
schedule, etc.

* Train for change. Practice being flexible by taking
different viewpoints, changing your routines
periodically, trying something new each day or week.

* Anticipate change. Learn all you can about
potential or upcoming change. Imagine your
responses to different options. Decide how you
might best adjust. Plan for changes in advance
whenever possible.

* Avoid impulsive changes. Evaluate all the pros and
cons of changes you are considering. Anticipate
problems and try to head them off in advance.

* Build safety zones. At times of major change or
clusters of change, create a sanctuary for yourself
with familiar routines and soothing environments.
Maintain an oasis of stability.

- **Use a wide-angle lens**. Try to look at the broad view of your current situation. Put it in historical perspective -- 50 years from now, who will care? Learn from the past -- "I know I'm a survivor!"

- **Be flexible**. Bend. Adapt. Flow with the necessary changes. Don't fight the inevitable. Allow the processes to unfold as they will -- even when they take unexpected directions.

- **Explore** change-related **meanings and feelings**. Think about your own reactions to the change. Self-awareness is a powerful ally in times of stress.

- **Ask advice from veterans**. Consult with others who have survived the changes you are currently experiencing. Learn their management secrets.

- **Let yourself grieve**. Grief accompanies any change as we let go of a past treasure (or even a past pain in the neck) and move into the uncertainty of a new direction. Take time to grieve. No matter how insignificant the loss seems, grief is a healing process.

- **Pace yourself**. Don't hurry through the process of change. You'll just add to your stress! Give yourself time to recover and rest. Take your time making decisions.

12) As a concluding exercise, the trainer invites participants to plan ahead for managing a specific anticipated change. He asks everyone to reflect on the following questions, using the back of a worksheet to record their responses.

   Note: Ask the questions one at a time, pausing long enough between them so that people have ample opportunity to reflect and write.

   ☐ As you look ahead and envision the changes you **wish** to make during the next few months -- as well as those that will probably happen to you anyway -- select one change that is likely to be troublesome for you. Write it down.

   ☐ What kind of adaptations and adjustments will you need to make because of that change? Record them.

   ☐ Describe the interpretations that will help you see this change in its most positive light.

□ What coping skills and strategies will be
particularly useful to you as you manage this
change?

□ How can you best prepare for this change? Make a
few preliminary notes toward a working plan for
dealing with the stress of this change.

13) If time allows, the trainer may invite participants to
share their plans with a neighbor or with the whole
group. He then may ask for reactions and insights to
the issues raised during the entire exercise.

VARIATIONS

■ The "Social Readjustment Rating Scale" (Holmes, TH and RH
Rahe [1967]. Journal of Psychosomatic Research, 11, 213-
218) could be utilized as the worksheet for Step 6 in place
of the worksheet provided. Please note that Holmes & Rahe's
scale is copyrighted and may not be duplicated without
permission from the publisher, Pergamon Press (New York).

■ Portions of this exercise could be used separately if time
does not allow for completion of the entire five-phase
process.

TRAINER'S NOTES

CHANGE CHECKLIST

Check the life changes you have experienced this year:

PERSONAL

- ☐ personal injury/illness, handicap
- ☐ pregnancy (yours or partner's)
- ☐ change in religious views/beliefs
- ☐ change in financial status
- ☐ change in self-concept
- ☐ ending a relationship
- ☐ change in emotional outlook
- ☐ change in roles
- ☐ buying/selling a car
- ☐ aging
- ☐ change in habits
  - ☐ alcohol   ☐ exercise
  - ☐ drugs   ☐ nutrition
  - ☐ tobacco
- ☐ other _____
  _____

FAMILY

- ☐ marriage
- ☐ family member(s) leaving home
- ☐ new family member(s)
- ☐ separation/divorce
- ☐ trouble with in-laws
- ☐ partner stopping/starting a job
- ☐ illness/healing of family member
- ☐ death of close friend or family member
- ☐ parent/child tensions
- ☐ change in recreation patterns
- ☐ other _____
  _____
  _____

WORK

- ☐ changed work load
- ☐ change in play
- ☐ starting new job
- ☐ promotion/demotion
- ☐ retirement
- ☐ change in hours
- ☐ change in relationships at work
- ☐ change in job security
- ☐ strike
- ☐ change in financial status
- ☐ other _____
  _____

ENVIRONMENT

- ☐ natural disaster
- ☐ moving to new:
  - ☐ house or apartment
  - ☐ neighborhood   ☐ climate
  - ☐ city   ☐ culture
- ☐ Christmas
- ☐ vacation
- ☐ remodeling
- ☐ war
- ☐ major house cleaning
- ☐ crime against property
- ☐ other _____
  _____

☐ Go back and mark the changes that required extra adaptation because of their importance to you.

☐ Identify one change that had a surprising effect on you:

☐ How did it affect you?

From D A Tubesing, **Kicking Your Stress Habits** (Duluth MN: Whole Person Associates, 1981)

CHANGES AND PERSONAL OUTLOOK

	HIGH STRESS CHANGE	LOW STRESS CHANGE
Event		
Adaptations/ Adjustments/ Other Changes Required		
Meanings/ Interpretations/ My Outlook		
In what ways does your interpretation of the change and what it will mean for you — your overall outlook — determine the amount of stress you will experience?		

83 JOB DESCRIPTIONS

Participants divide into separate male and female groups to examine how sex role stereotyping can lead to the interpersonal stress of conflicting expectations.

GOALS

1) To demonstrate role conflict as a source of stress.

2) To study role stereotypes that can cause stress and interfere with interpersonal communication.

3) To present attitude awareness as a technique in stress management.

GROUP SIZE

Designed for use in groups of 8 to 20 people, adaptable for larger groups. It works best with groups who are motivated to look at this issue in their work setting.

TIME FRAME

60 minutes

PHYSICAL SETTING

Two adjoining rooms or a larger room with a divider so that two subgroups can meet privately.

MATERIALS NEEDED

Two copies of the POSITIONS ANNOUNCEMENT worksheet for each participant.

PROCESS

1) The trainer begins by distributing two copies of the POSITION ANNOUNCEMENT to all participants and explaining that everyone will be asked individually and in groups to write two job descriptions -- one for their own sex, and one for members of the opposite sex.

2) Participants are instructed to begin by using one POSITION ANNOUNCEMENT outline to write a job description for the opposite sex. Men describe the position requirements and qualifications for being "a woman". Women set forth the requirements and qualifications for being "a man." (5-10 minutes)

3) The trainer announces that after he gives the next set
   of instructions, all the men will form one group and
   move to the adjacent room for their discussion. All the
   women will stay in this room and form their own
   discussion group.

   The trainer describes the process each group will follow
   during the next 15 minutes:

   * Designate one person as the group's recorder.
   * Participants should share the job descriptions they
     have written for the opposite sex.
   * Based on these individual responses, each group
     should construct a composite "ideal" job description
     for the opposite sex. The male group constructs the
     "ideal" description for being a woman, the female
     group constructs the "ideal" description for being a
     man.

   *Note: If possible, moderate one subgroup and utilize a
          colleague to moderate the other. If a subgroup is
          larger than 10 people, divide it into smaller
          discussion units to allow for more participation.*

4) After 15 minutes, the trainer announces to each group
   that the process of Steps 1 and 2 are going to be repeated, except this time they will be asked to write and
   discuss job descriptions for members of their own sex.

   First, participants individually design a job description for their own sex. (5-10 min)

   After 10 minutes, groups are instructed to construct a
   "real" (not an "ideal") job description for their own
   sex.   The male group develops a "real" description for
   men, the female group designs a "real" description for
   women. (15 min)

   *Note: During this entire process men and women remain in
          separate work areas where they will not influence
          each other.*

5) The trainer reassembles the total group and asks the
   recorder from one group to read the "ideal" job
   description devised by their group for the opposite sex.
   The trainer asks how many members of the other group
   feel they would qualify for this position, given the
   description.

   The same process is repeated for the other group. The
   recorder reads the "ideal" description and members of
   the target group are polled on their suitability for the
   job.

The trainer elicits comments and reactions from both groups and facilitates a general discussion about role stereotyping and its stressful effects in interpersonal relationships.

5) Recorders from both groups read the "real" job descriptions composed by each sex and participants are asked to compare the real and ideal roles portrayed by these descriptions of the sexes.

The trainer invites participants to reflect on how they could use insights from this experience in managing stress better in their own lives. She solicits examples of specific applications and highlights the importance of attitude awareness in successful stress management.

VARIATIONS

- This exercise could easily be adapted for other stress-provoking role stereotype situations. Instead of composing "real" and "ideal" job descriptions for men and women, use roles such as parent/teenager, father/mother, worker/supervisor, executive/secretary etc.

TRAINER'S NOTES

Submitted by Randy R Weigel.

POSITION ANNOUNCEMENT
Job Description

Position Title

Major Responsibilities of Position

Required Qualifications

Desirable

Must Be Willing To

Fringe Benefits Include

84 THE LAST CHRISTMAS TREE

This fantasy exercise enables participants to explore the stress associated with rejection. It is most effective at the beginning of a learning experience.

GOALS

1) To identify the stress of actual or potential rejection.

2) To stimulate discussion about the feelings of being "left out".

3) To discover alternative perceptions of the rejection experience.

GROUP SIZE

Works best with small groups (6-10 people), but can easily be adapted for larger or smaller groups.

TIME FRAME

20-30 minutes

MATERIALS NEEDED

THE LAST CHRISTMAS TREE worksheets for everyone.

PROCESS

Note: This experience may evoke strong feelings in some participants. If your group is too large or if your time frame is too short to respond compassionately to someone who vividly recollects a traumatic memory, modify the depth of this exercise by shortening the fantasy.

1) The trainer introduces the exercise as a fantasy journey to explore one common source of stress -- rejection. She invites participants to settle comfortably in their chairs and close their eyes.

   Note: For best effect, dim the lights and eliminate (or minimize) outside stimuli.

2) As a warm-up, the trainer leads the group through any familiar breathing/relaxation sequence. (5 minutes)

3) Once everyone has settled down and relaxed, the trainer guides the group on an imaginary journey to a Christmas

tree lot.   Participants are instructed to imagine they
are Christmas trees, waiting to be sold.

The trainer encourages participants to be as vivid and
detailed as possible as they imagine themselves in this
place.   She helps people set the scene by slowly asking
questions such as those below.

*Note: This is an open fantasy experience.   The questions
      are designed to facilitate the visualization
      process.   Give people plenty of time to play with
      the images in each segment.*

   * *Picture the lot in your mind.   Where is it?   On a
     street corner?   In a back yard?   Out in the country?
     In a parking lot?*

   * *What time of day is it?   What's the weather like?
     What can you smell?   What do you see around you?
     What sounds do you hear?*

   * *What kind of tree are you?   Spruce?   Pine?   Balsam?
     What size are you?   What shape?*

   * *How many other trees are there with you?   Are you
     thrown in a pile?   Crowded in?   Leaning on a brace?
     Or stuck in a snowbank?*

Once everyone seems involved in the fantasy, the trainer
directs participants to visualize many people coming to
examine the trees.

   * *Imagine that each person looks over the trees and
     makes a selection, but you are not chosen.*

   * *How do people decide which tree to buy?   What do
     they say?*

   * *How do you feel as one-by-one, each of the other
     trees is selected and you are left behind, all alone
     -- the last Christmas tree?*

*Note: Don't rush.   People will need time to experience
      the impact of not being picked.*

In conclusion, the trainer invites participants to take
a few moments in silence to go with the flow of their
imagination.   They are directed to visualize a
conclusion to their fantasy.

   * *What happens next?   How does the story end?*

   * *When you are finished, open your eyes.*

4) When several people have opened their eyes, the trainer
    distributes LAST CHRISTMAS TREE worksheets to all. She
    invites participants to recall their visualization and
    jot down some notes about it:

    ❑ In Box A, write down any negative images or feelings
       you remember from the visualization. How did it
       feel to be looked over and never taken -- left for
       last? What stress did you experience?

    ❑ In Box B, record any positive images and feelings
       you noticed during the imaginary journey. Were
       there any good feelings or positive outcomes from
       the process of being left for last?

    ❑ In Box C, briefly outline your ending to the
       fantasy.

5) The trainer solicits examples of positive and negative
    feelings experienced by the group and uses these to
    stimulate discussion about the stress of "rejection"
    versus the possible advantages of perceiving this
    experience as being "set aside".

    She goes on to note that everyone, at times, shares the
    experience of the rejected Christmas tree (eg, not being
    chosen for a team, no date for the prom, not getting a
    job, losing an election, feeling left out at a party).

    Participants are asked to recall some of their own
    rejection experiences and make note of a few in Box D on
    the worksheet.

    After a few minutes, the trainer invites participants to
    look over their list of rejections, to remember how they
    coped with these situations and to jot down a phrase or
    two describing their coping style for each rejection
    experience.

6) Each participant is then invited to describe briefly his
    images during the visualization and then to read/share
    his ending. (5-10 minutes)

7) After everyone has had a turn, the trainer opens the
    floor to discussion of real life rejection experiences
    and how people have coped with them. (5-10 minutes)

    *Note: For added interest, ask participants to consider
          how their ending to the visualization fits with
          their style of handling the stress of rejection.*

VARIATIONS

- Any similar visualization of potential rejection (eg, toys
  in a store, oranges on a peddlar's cart, etc) could be
  substituted for the Christmas tree image.

- In a group of more than 8 people, divide into triads for
  sharing in Steps 6 and 7. Break the process into two
  segments and keep time for the groups -- 5 minutes to share
  stories and 5-10 minutes to explore rejection experiences and
  coping strategies.

TRAINER'S NOTES

Submitted by Marcia A Schnorr.

THE LAST CHRISTMAS TREE

A NEGATIVE FEELINGS

B POSITIVE FEELINGS

C MY CONCLUSION:

D

MANAGEMENT STRATEGIES

85 METAPHORS (p 49)

Participants study the form and function of various objects, seeking clues to creative stress management. (40-50 minutes)

86 S.O.S. FOR STRESS (p 54)

Participants learn an overarching paradigm for coping with stress and apply the specific strategies from this model to a personal stressor of their choice. (30-50 minutes)

87 STRESS CLUSTERS CLINIC (p 59)

In this thought-provoking card game participants utilize separate decks of stressor cards and coping cards to create stress scenarios and strategies for coping based on "the luck of the draw." (40-60 minutes)

88 CORPORATE PRESENTATION (p 66)

In this affirming small group activity, participants give themselves a lecture about the ten best methods for managing stress. (20-30 minutes)

89 IMAGINE SUCCESS (p 68)

Participants practice the technique of positive visualization, imagining themselves as successfully employing a selected coping skill. (15-30 minutes)

85 METAPHORS

Participants study the form and function of various objects, seeking clues to creative stress management.

GOALS

1) To provide a model for back-home problem solving.

2) To promote creativity and non-linear approaches to stress management.

GROUP SIZE

Unlimited

TIME FRAME

40-50 minutes

MATERIALS NEEDED

METAPHORS worksheets for all; a brown paper bag for each group, filled with 6-8 objects familiar to all participants (eg, file folders, transistor radio, car keys, ID badge, paycheck, telephone, toothbrush, paperclips, salt shaker, credit card, etc).

PROCESS

1) The trainer introduces the exercise by highlighting the importance of creativity in stressful situations -- for changing perceptions and for generating alternative solutions.

- When we're stuck we can't think of new approaches for dealing with our stressors. Our lack of new ideas limits us and lowers our energy.

- A new perspective can reduce stress and increase vitality even if the situation itself doesn't change. New ideas almost always bring renewed energy for facing the problems that surround us.

- Common everyday items can stimulate our creativity by serving as metaphors for coping.

- Here's how the process works. First we will notice and describe the <u>form</u> and <u>function</u> of the item:
  □ What is it like? How is it made? (form)
  □ How is it used? What does it do? (function)

- Next we ask the force fit question:
  - ☐ What can this item, with all its unique qualities, teach us about stress and how to manage it more effectively?

- This "force fit" activity generates new creative approaches to coping by stimulating a whole new mindset.

2) To illustrate this process the trainer chooses an object in the room (eg, piece of chalk) and asks participants to help describe characteristics of its design and form (cylindrical, smooth hard surface, fits easily in hand, flakes off on board but not on hands, color visible on contrasting background, brittle, etc).

These attributes are recorded on the board until 20 or more have been suggested. The trainer then poses the force fit metaphor question:

- ☐ What can the form of this object teach us about stress and/or how to manage it better?

    Note: Responses might include ideas such as: "Its cylindrical shape reminds us that we need to be well-rounded." "We, like the chalk, need a smooth hard surface so that criticism does not dent." "We need to show ourselves off to good advantage by picking the background against which we shine." "Like the brittle chalk we need a stiff backbone as well as a stiff upper lip." "Maybe I need to be more slippery -- or grate on someone's nerves!"

3) The trainer next asks the group to generate a list describing the possible functions or uses of this object (eg, draw hopscotch, record information on neutral surface, mark location for hemline, coat a plumbline, etc).

After 15-20 functions are named, the trainer again poses the force fit metaphor question:

- ☐ How could these functions apply to stress and/or managing it better?

    Note: Responses might include ideas such as: "When chalk is used for teaching, it wears itself out. We need to 'give ourselves' to our tasks, too!" "Like the message that was written, read and erased, our troubles do pass eventually -- they are erased." "Chalk has a single purpose -- to communicate! So do we!"

© 1986 Whole Person Press PO Box 3151 Duluth MN 55803

4) The trainer divides the participants into small groups of 6-8 people. He gives each person a METAPHORS worksheet and instructs them to select a current stressor for which they want to generate a new viewpoint or additional coping options. Participants write this stressor at the top of their worksheet.

5) The trainer gives every group a bag of objects and instructs participants to each draw out one object from the bag. Individually participants follow the process demonstrated in Steps 2 and 3 to identify the form and function of their object and to "force fit" it onto their stressor as they search for creative options, recording their personal observations in Boxes A, B and C on the worksheet. (5 minutes)

6) Participants are instructed to glance around the room and select for their next focus some object that intrigues them. Participants follow the same process as before, identifying form and functions, then seeking alternative perceptions and creative coping strategies from the "force fit" process. They record their observations in Boxes D, E and F of the worksheet. (5 minutes)

7) One-by-one participants share their insights within their small groups. Each person takes one minute to share and then receives one or two minutes of "creative additions" from the group. These additional coping ideas are then recorded in the right-hand column (Boxes G and H) of the worksheet. (2-3 minutes for each participant, about 15 minutes total)

8) The trainer reconvenes the entire group and points out that common items for use as "force fit" metaphors are around us all the time waiting to spark our creativity and to enhance our coping capacity.

VARIATION

■ To reduce the time required, divide into 3- or 4-person groups for Step 7. This may lower the creativity and the energy level of participants.

TRAINER'S NOTES

METAPHORS

Please identify one stressor in your life that makes you feel "stuck in a rut," and for which you would like to discover some additional ideas for coping . . .

_____

(the stressor I will focus on)

A OBJECT FROM THE BAG	C FUNCTION
	(How is it used? What does it do?)
B FORM/DESIGN (What is it like? Characteristics?)	

E OBJECT FROM THE ROOM	G FUNCTION
	(How is it used? What does it do?)
F FORM/DESIGN (What is it like? Characteristics?)	

COMMENTS AND REACTIONS:

FORCE FIT D	**BRAINSTORM** I
How could I apply this to my stress?	Additional ideas from my group

FORCE FIT H	**BRAINSTORM** J
How could I apply this to my stress?	

Circle the three ideas that are most intriguing to you.

86 S.O.S. FOR STRESS

Participants learn an overarching paradigm for coping with
stress and apply the specific strategies from this model to
a personal stressor of their choice.

GOALS

1) To expand awareness of coping options.

2) To demonstrate the variety of coping approaches that
   could prove effective for any single stressor.

3) To encourage the use of under-utilized or neglected
   skills for managing stress.

GROUP SIZE

Unlimited

TIME FRAME

30–50 minutes

MATERIALS NEEDED

Blank paper for all participants.

PROCESS

1) The trainer introduces the exercise with a few brief
   comments on stress and coping which set the stage for
   the SOS -- Success Over Stress -- coping paradigm.

   ● The stress reaction is commonly fueled from two
     sources -- the external events that impinge on our
     lives and our internal reactions to those events.

   ● Since the source of stress is both internal (from
     within us) and external (provoked by our physical/
     interpersonal environment), the complete range of
     stress management strategies calls for us to alter
     our internal reactions as well as to control the
     external precipitators that initiate the stress
     cycle. When neither of these options proves parti-
     cularly effective, we may activate a third strategy
     -- gathering support from our environment.

2) The trainer distributes a sheet of paper to each participant. He asks everyone to choose a current stressor
   in their life that they would like to cope with more

effectively. Participants record their stressful situation in the upper left-hand corner.

*Note: For purposes of this exercise, participants should
select a stressor of moderate to major impact in
their lives. Minor stressors such as "an office
mate who crunches apples too loudly," or "anger
that I burned the eggs," are not recommended.
Better to choose an issue of significance that
could benefit from the concentrated attention it
will receive during this exercise.*

3) The trainer explains that he will be presenting three
different SOS -- Success Over Stress -- strategies,
describing several different coping skills and asking
them to apply these alternative approaches to the stress
that they have listed.

*Note: As you outline the chalktalk points one at a time,
suggest that people take notes on the strategies,
using the left-hand side of the paper, and leaving
room to answer the related coping application
questions to the right.*

4) The trainer introduces SOS Strategy #1 -- S̲TART O̲N (the)
S̲ITUATION.

He notes that most people identify stress both with
major life changes such as divorce or a layoff and with
the myriad of tasks, demands, frustrations, conflicts,
worries and hassles that plague them on a day-to-day
basis. A primary approach to managing such stressful
situations is to tackle them head on -- to work at
changing the external circumstance that is provoking the
stress reaction.

The trainer describes several skills that are useful in
working on the external source of stress and asks participants to reflect on how each approach might apply to
their identified situation.

*Note: Be sure to expand the chalktalk notes with addi-
tional details and your own examples so that the
concepts come alive. Allow plenty of time for
people to answer each "application" question.*

- Set limits. Establish priorities. Eliminate some
activities. Simplify where possible. Schedule
necessities. Refuse unreasonable demands. Choose
your battles carefully.
    □ What limits do you need to set in order to cope
    more effectively?

- Take charge. Take responsibility for your predica-
  ment. Do something specific. Reduce uncertainty --
  seek additional information. Face choices. Make
  decisions. Be assertive.
    □ In what ways could you take charge of your situ-
      ation? What, specifically, do you need to do?

- Minimize change. Stay put. Keep to a schedule.
  Postpone decisions. Lay low -- cruise in neutral
  for a while.
    □ How would minimizing change help you cope with
      your stressor? What changes can you postpone?

The trainer invites everyone to reflect on their applications of the START ON (the) SITUATION Strategy, asking
them to respond in writing to the following questions:

  □ What can you change about your current situation?
    How could you go about it?

5) The trainer presents the SOS Strategy #2 -- START ON
    SELF.

    He notes that stress never occurs without our "coopera-
    tion." Our response to stressors ultimately determines
    the level of stress we experience. Often we have more
    control over ourselves and our reactions than we do over
    the circumstances in which we find ourselves.

    Participants are invited to consider several skills for
    altering their internal response. The trainer guides
    them in applying each approach to their stressor.

    - Take care of yourself. Get adequate rest, slow
      down, utilize deep breathing, relax regularly,
      develop present-awareness, establish a daily rou-
      tine, find quiet time, watch your physical health.
        □ How would taking better care of yourself help
          with your stress? What do you need to do to
          take better care of yourself?

    - Get away from it all. Change your environment.
      Find a new spot to think, work, play, live. Develop
      external interests. Give yourself rewarding breaks.
      Exercise regularly.
        □ How could you "get away" from your stressor for
          a while?

    - Strengthen your resistance. Use antidotes to
      stress. Learn to tolerate uncertainty. Identify
      your wants and preferences and learn to satisfy
      them. Revise your unspoken rules and negative self-
      messages.

    □ How could strengthening your resistance help you
      cope with your stress?

● Get your mental house in order. Anticipate change.
  Develop your skills and competencies. Resolve your
  conflicts. Clarify your values. Focus your attention on what really counts.
    □ What would a clearer, stronger mind do to help
      you cope? How could you move in this direction?

The trainer asks participants to review their responses
to the START ON SELF Strategy and summarize in writing
their answers to the questions below:

  □ Overall, what do you need to start doing to better
    care for yourself? What difference would this make
    for you in handling your stress?

6) **The trainer describes the final SOS strategy, SEARCH OUT
SUPPORT.**

He suggests that even if we have tried to change the
situations and we've already done as much as we can to
take care of ourself and go it alone, there's still more
we can do. Our environment is chock full of resources
(friends, experts, rituals, connections) that can support us during times of stress -- if we only seek them
out and take advantage of their strength.

The trainer outlines several networking approaches that
might be effective in managing stress and invites
participants to apply them in their own situations.

● Utilize your environment. Reach out for resources.
  Work within your context. Take advantage of your
  surroundings. Let your space protect and comfort
  you. Search out beauty.
    □ What resources in your environment have you
      neglected? How could tapping into the support
      of your environment help with your stress?

● Share your burden. Lean on someone you trust. Talk
  it out. Ask for help. Accept the comfort and
  encouragement of friends. Find a support group.
    □ Who could share your burden? How could that
      support help you with your stress?

● Call out the horses. Connect with the experts.
  Seek counsel and advice from professional resources
  in your community or workplace.
    □ What expertise could you call on in dealing with
      your particular stress? What stops you from
      asking for help?

● Don't suffer on the sidelines. Create support
  systems where they don't exist. Participate in
  ritual. Share others' experience. Support someone
  else. Make connections.
  □ How would getting involved again help you cope
    with your stress? What should you "jump into"?

The trainer invites participants to review their
networking strategies in response to the following
questions:

□ What resources around you can you call on for
  support? How would it help you to do so?

7) The trainer suggests that the three SOS strategies, no
   matter how brilliantly outlined, will not be effective
   unless we are ready to get going!

The trainer challenges participants to apply what they
have learned in this exercise about coping by making a
plan and preparing to take some action. He guides them
through the process using the sequence of questions
below:

□ Look over all your comments on each separate coping
  skill, as well as the three major SOS strategies.
  Which SOS strategy shows the most promise for your
  situation?
□ What, specifically, should you / will you do first?
□ What's your next step in coping?
□ What must you do now to improve your coping style?

8) The trainer asks for a general sharing of insights and
   observations gained by participants during the process
   of this exercise.

VARIATIONS

■ If time permits the trainer may divide participants into
  small discussion groups for sharing of insights and action
  plans as part of Step 9.

■ The trainer could provide a worksheet that outlines the SOS
  strategies and specific skills in each. Participants mark
  their worksheets rather than taking notes. The convenience
  to participants may be offset by their tendency to "race
  through" the separate skills without carefully considering
  each one on its own merit.

The skills outlined in this exercise are adapted from James
Mills, Coping with Stress (New York: John Wiley & Sons, 1982).

87 STRESS CLUSTERS

In this thought-provoking card game participants utilize separate decks of stressor cards and coping cards to create stress scenarios and strategies for coping based on "the luck of the draw."

GOALS

1) To explore the stress generated by clusters of change.

2) To apply specific coping skills to a life-like stress scenario.

3) To promote problem-solving approaches to coping with stress.

TIME FRAME

40-60 minutes

MATERIALS NEEDED

One STRESS SCENARIO worksheet for each team (6-8 participants); one complete deck of PILEUP cards for every three teams (18-24 people total). The PILEUP card game is available from Whole Person Press, PO Box 3151, Duluth MN 55803.

This process works best when each team of participants can gather around a table to work together.

GROUP SIZE

The exercise is described for 18-24 people but can easily be adapted for larger or smaller groups by adjusting the size and number of work teams. It is essential to have at least three teams, but they could range in size from three to eight participants.

PROCESS

Note: Before beginning this exercise the trainer should familiarize herself with the PILEUP cards and separate each deck into three piles: 1) the yellow "stressor" cards; 2) the red and green "coper" cards; and 3) the rainbow "creative" cards. Each pile should be shuffled thoroughly.

1) The trainer briefly describes the process of the exercise, noting that teams will create a profile of a hypothetical person under stress who has experienced a

random cluster of life events, much like we are often
dealt in life. Teams will then exchange scenarios and
develop creative coping strategies to deal with the
clusters of change.

2) The trainer divides participants into at least three
teams of 6-8 people each.

   *Note: To randomize the group composition divide
   according to vowels in participants' first names.
   Ask all those who have an "A" in their first name
   to stand up and collect themselves in one area of
   the room as a team. Repeat with "E"s, "I"s, "O"s,
   "U"s and "Y"s. If some groups are too large,
   split them up by some other alphabetical criteria.
   If some groups are too small, instruct "leftovers"
   from one vowel team to join those of another,
   ensuring that there are at least three teams and
   each of them ultimately has 6-8 members.*

3) Once all the teams have assembled and found a workspace
in the room, the trainer directs team members to
introduce themselves to each other and then select a
team name (eg, "Stress Busters," "The A Team," "Coping
Clowns," etc) and appoint a team recorder. (5 minutes)

   *Note: While teams are getting acquainted, the trainer
   needs to go around from team to team, giving each
   group a pile of stressor cards equal to the number
   of people on the team. These should be placed
   face down on the table along with one STRESS
   CLUSTERS CLINIC worksheet and an admonition not to
   "peek" until you give the word.*

4) <u>Stress Clusters</u>. The trainer calls time and invites
each person to draw one card from the stress pileup,
explaining that every card describes one or two life
events that can cause stress or strain.

   She instructs participants to take turns reading the
   information on their cards. As each person reads the
   stressors indicated on his card, the group chooses one
   event from the card that will be added to the team's
   stress cluster. The card is then placed face up on the
   table and the recorder writes down the selected
   stressor in the top left box of the worksheet.

   Once all the cards have been placed on the table, the
   team summarizes their "pileup" of stressors and adds any
   other changes that would probably accompany this stress
   cluster. (For example, if the pileup includes "move to
   a new city", it is very likely that other changes --
   such as "new home," "change in schools," "new friendship

patterns," etc -- would also occur.) The recorder adds these associated stressors to the team list.

5) After 3-5 minutes, the trainer interrupts the process and directs teams to brainstorm a scenario of a hypothetical person under stress who has experienced the entire cluster of life change events represented by the team's "pileup." She encourages them to imagine as many specific details as they can, and to make the story as true to life as possible.

As the scenario unfolds, the recorder notes all of the ideas generated and once the team has decided on their final scenario, he writes it down on the worksheet. (8-10 minutes)

Note: Remind recorders to write legibly and in narrative style so that the next team will be able to read the story easily. You may want to offer an example such as the one below -- or better yet, make up your own from a random deal of stressors.

Stressor cards: "death of a family member," "loss of job," "increased hassles with the kids over use of the car," "Christmas," "troubles with the boss" and "increased alcohol consumption."

Scenario: Tom's mother died suddenly six weeks ago after a long illness that had depleted the family bank account and sapped their emotional and physical energy. Jan, Tom's wife, quit her job to help care for his mom -- which has meant they got behind on car payments. Tom's boss is giving him trouble for taking time off and not being available for weekend work. He's started drinking regularly to unwind at the end of the day. All of Tom's siblings came for Christmas, since they knew it would be Mom's last. It was an exhausting holiday, with lots of intense conversations and late evenings as well as arguments about putting Mom in a home. Tom and Jan are concerned about 16-year old Jason's group of friends and their Friday night hot-rodding. So far they've refused Jason's requests for the car on weekends, but he is bugging them for more driving privileges.

6) As the teams are finishing up their scenarios, the trainer circulates and gives each group a pack of coping cards, equal in number to the team members. These are placed face down in a stack on the table. She announces "one minute to finish up," waits a moment or two and then calls everyone's attention.

7) Coping Strategies. Recorders are instructed to "dump"
    their completed stress scenarios on the neighboring team
    (clockwise) who will be challenged to cope with it.

    *Note: As the worksheets are passed on, encourage the
          teams to verbalize the challenge with comments
          such as, "Here -- find a foolproof solution for
          this mess!"*

8) The trainer directs the teams to select someone to read
    to the other team members the scenario they have just
    received.

    When all the teams are done, the trainer announces that
    the new pile of cards on the table represents the coping
    resources available to the hypothetical person in their
    scenario. Some are positive copers (green cards) that
    are often effective for dealing with stress -- and some
    are negative or questionable copers (red cards) that may
    temporarily relieve stress, but have undesirable side
    effects.

    She instructs everyone to draw a coping card from the
    pile and one-by-one read the information contained on
    the card, including the skill name and the examples of
    how it might be used. After each card is read, it is
    placed face-up on the table, the recorder writes it on
    the right-hand side of the middle section of the work-
    sheet and the group brainstorms ideas about how this
    particular coping strategy could prove useful in manag-
    ing the stress of this new scenario. The same process is
    repeated for each coping card. (8-10 minutes)

    *Note: Encourage groups to explore potential positive and
          negative results of using the red negative copers
          and the many alternative options for activating
          each of the green positive copers.*

9) After 8-10 minutes the trainer interrupts the process
    and directs each group to incorporate the multitude of
    coping ideas they have generated into a comprehensive
    management plan for dealing with the stress scenario
    that was dumped on them. The recorder writes down the
    details of the coping plan on the worksheet. (5 minutes)

    *Note: While groups are finishing up, go around and give
          each team two rainbow cards, dealt face down on
          the table.*

10) Creative Twists. Once again the trainer instructs each
    group to pass their stress scenario worksheet (complete
    with coping plan) to the neighboring group (clockwise).
    In each team one person reads both the stress scenario

written by the original group and the coping strategy
developed by the second team.

When the teams are finished reading, the trainer
announces that the final two cards are "wild" cards --
designed to help stretch participants' imagination and
stimulate creative approaches to coping. She directs
the teams to read the rainbow "wild" cards they were
dealt and use the creative problem solving questions
listed on each to generate unusual applications and
creative twists to the coping scenario they have
received. (5-8 minutes)

> *Note: Encourage people to be as creative and "off-the-wall" as possible in suggesting whatever outrageous possibilities cross their minds. Suggest that the teams work quickly, producing a steady stream of ideas as rapidly as possible.*

The team recorder lists all the creative twists at the
bottom of the worksheet.

11) The trainer reconvenes the entire group and asks the
     group recorders, one-by-one, to read their worksheets,
     including the stress scenario written by the first
     group, the coping strategies suggested by the second and
     selected highlights from the creative twists added by
     their own team. (6-10 minutes)

12) In closing, the trainer may solicit from participants
     their insights and observations about stress clusters,
     creative coping strategies and the process of this
     exercise.

VARIATIONS

- The yellow stressor cards include numbers (representing
  research data on the relative amount of stress caused by
  each change) and symbols signifying the category of stressor
  (eg, family strain, financial, transitions, etc). As part
  of Step 4 teams could analyze the types and severity of
  their stress cluster and compare that distribution with
  other teams.

- The coping cards are divided into six categories of positive
  skills (physical, mental, spiritual, family, interpersonal
  and diversion), as well as 14 negative coping activities.
  As part of Step 8 teams could analyze the various types of
  coping strategies represented by the cards they have drawn
  and discuss the importance of cultivating a wide variety of
  coping alternatives.

STRESS CLUSTERS CLINIC

STRESS SCENARIO

Here's the person and the situation:

Stressors we drew:

COPING STRETEGY

Coping cards we drew

Here's how we suggest handling it:

CREATIVE TWISTS WE RECOMMEND

Rainbow cards we drew:

88 CORPORATE PRESENTATION

In this affirming small group activity, participants give
themselves a lecture about the ten best methods for managing
stress.

GOALS

1) To tap into participants' wisdom about coping with
    stress.

2) To provide an overview of stress management strategies.

GROUP SIZE

Described for 30-60 people, but works well with smaller
groups, too.

TIME FRAME

20-30 minutes

MATERIALS NEEDED

Newsprint and markers for each small group; flip chart or
blackboard for the trainer.

PROCESS

1) The trainer announces that during the next half hour
    participants will be searching for a wide spectrum of
    coping strategies that might be helpful in managing
    stress.

    He notes that everyone is an expert on coping -- since
    we all successfully manage a steady stream of potential
    stressors day by day across our lifetime. During this
    exercise participants will join in creating a corporate
    presentation that draws upon the collected wisdom of the
    group.

2) Participants are instructed to take out a dollar bill (a
    five or ten is fine, too), look at the bill and notice
    the last digit of the serial number. The trainer
    designates different spots in the room for each numeral
    (0 to 9) and asks people to gather in the appointed area
    that matches their digit.

    *Note: This should create small groups of 3-6 people.
    The groups can be uneven, but combine groups, if
    necessary, so that none has fewer than 3 or 4*

*members. If the whole class is less than 30
people, decide how many groups (4 to 6 people
each) are needed and then divide by combining last
digits. For two groups separate by odd and even
serial numbers. For five groups, divide in pairs
(0-1, 2-3, etc). Or if you can't figure all this
out, use some other method to form small groups.*

3) Once all the groups are settled, the trainer challenges
participants to give themselves a lecture on the topic:
THE TEN BEST STRATEGIES FOR COPING WITH STRESS. He
encourages each group to draw out the wisdom of its
members, making sure everyone has input and recording
all their ideas on newsprint. (15 minutes)

4) The trainer directs the groups to spend the next 5
minutes looking over their list and determining which
coping methods they think are most effective in dealing
with stress.

5) The trainer reconvenes the entire group and announces
that it's now time for the corporate presentation.
Participants are invited to share their answers to the
question, "What are the ten best strategies for coping
with stress?".

The trainer encourages participants to "build a case"
for the potency and value of the copers they suggest and
notes that he will also help with the presentation by
putting in his two cents worth along the way.

As people volunteer their insights, the trainer records
the ideas on the board -- expanding, amplifying,
connecting, integrating, challenging where appropriate
-- and for each contribution, thanks the presenter.

*Note: If participants seem reluctant to speak up, try a
little contest between groups or offer a reward
for everyone who contributes.*

6) The trainer builds on the data base generated by the
group to present his own schema of the most effective
strategies for managing stress.

VARIATION

■ If time permits before Step 6, the group is instructed to
reach a consensus on the 10 best coping ideas suggested.
The trainer then facilitates an energetic discussion around
this issue.

Submitted by Joel Goodman.

89 IMAGINE SUCCESS

Participants practice the technique of positive
visualization, imagining themselves as successfully
employing a selected coping skill.

GOALS

1) To increase the probability of successful stress
   management through the use of positive visualizaiton.

2) To apply a practical principle of stress management
   within the learning experience.

GROUP SIZE

Unlimited; also effective for use with individuals.

TIME FRAME

15-30 minutes

PROCESS

*Note: This exercise most appropriately follows a presenta-
tion in which participants have examined the multitude
of positive coping strategies available to them.*

1) Participants are asked to identify one stressor they
   would particularly like to manage better and to choose
   one strategy presented during the learning experience
   that they imagine might be effective in coping with that
   stressor.

   *Note: Give a few examples (ideally drawn from previous
   discussion in the group) before asking participants to write down the single stressor and
   specific coping activity they have selected.*

2) The trainer prepares the group by briefly describing the
   exercise and "walking through" the steps of the positive
   visualization process, answering any questions that may
   arise.

   She then provides a theoretical framework for "imaging
   success":

   ● Behavioral theory postulates that if we can imagine
     ourselves successfully changing our behavior, we are
     more likely to follow through on that new behavior
     in everyday life. The positive visualization you

will experience in this exercise is a process of "thinking" your way into new ways of acting and being.

- Imaging is more powerful than willpower. If you first imagine yourself experiencing success with a new skill, you are far more likely, in fact, to be successful when you put that skill into practice.

- World-class athletes in every sport use positive visualization to improve their concentration and performance. The same process will work for you if you want to improve your record as a stress manager!

3) The trainer asks people to get comfortable in their chairs, or to move around the room and find a place where they can relax fully. She invites them to loosen any tight clothing such as ties, belts, etc.

   Note: Pause to allow time for this position change and "settling in".

4) As soon as everyone is settled, the trainer guides participants through the positive visualization process, using statements and questions similar to those included in the IMAGINE SUCCESS script below.

5) After people have completed the visualization, the trainer divides participants into triads to share their experiences with each other.

   Participants are instructed to describe their visualization as if they are retelling a dream -- slowly drawing the scene, then embellishing it with the feelings they experienced. She encourages everyone to concentrate on how they successfully coped with their stress by using their selected coping skills.

   Note: It is important to acknowledge that some people may have had difficulty imaging the scene and their success with stress. Emphasize that visualization is also a skill that becomes easier with practice. Encourage people to try again with another coping skill -- some strategies may work better than others in real life -- and in visualization! Reassure people who "didn't quite get into this" so that they don't feel like failures! This exercise is designed to help people feel successful!

VARIATIONS

- During or after Step 5 invite participants -- in triads or as a large group -- to share the coping skill they selected and to articulate the positive change they imagine will happen in their lives as they begin to utilize this skill more fully.

- To close the exercise, participants write a set of recommendations for themselves, based on their visualization experience. This could take the form of a behavioral contract or an inspirational letter to be mailed to themselves at the end of the learning experience.

TRAINER'S NOTES

Submitted by Sally G Strosahl.

IMAGINE SUCCESS

Close your eyes . . . take some deep breaths . . . tune out the noises and the people around you . . . focus on yourself

> Note: Pause and model these instructions by taking several deep breaths yourself, sighing and slowing your voice.

Now I'd like you to think about the <u>stressor</u> *you selected as your focus . . . Recall it . . . Bring it to life right now . . . (Pause)*

> *Say to yourself, "I feel very stressed when   (your stressor)   happens in my life . . ." (Pause)*

> *Imagine how your whole self responds to this stress. Feel all your stress symptoms . . . (Pause)*

> *How do you feel? . . . (Pause)*

> *Allow yourself to imagine all the pain that stress brings you . . . (Pause)*

Now recall the <u>coping skill</u> *you selected . . . Imagine how this skill can help you deal creatively with the stressor. (Pause)*

> *Say to yourself, "When I feel stressed, I will successfully use   (your skill)   for myself to relieve and cope with my stress. It will help me a great deal. . . " (Pause)*

> *Imagine yourself practicing this skill. Actually envision how you look . . . how your body feels . . . and exactly how you act out this skill . . . (Pause)*

>> *What are you doing? . . . How does it feel? . . How do you feel? . . . (Pause)*

>> *How does your body feel? . . . (Pause)*

> *Imagine yourself successfully coping with your stress using this skill . . . Watch yourself dealing with your stress . . . (Pause)*

>> *What happens to your stress? . . . (Pause)*

Observe the positive effects that extend to other areas of your life . . . (Pause)

Imagine yourself successfully coping with your stress. . (Pause)

Feel the relief and positive energy that flows through you as you become aware of your ability to cope and to feel better . . . (Pause)

Hold on to your good feelings . . . Be confident that you can, in fact, take charge of the stress in your life . . . (Pause)

Now, begin preparing yourself to end this exercise . . . Come back into an awareness of the room where you are now. (Pause)

Slowly move a few muscles, stretch and take another deep breath . . . (Pause)

Then slowly open you eyes and begin to notice your surroundings . . . (Pause)

Note: Repeat these instructions as necessary until all have "come back into the room".

SKILL BUILDERS

90 CONFLICT MANAGEMENT (p 73)

In this thought-provoking learning experience participants explore four conflict-prevention skills and experiment with applying them to specific conflict situations. (60 minutes)

91 EIGHT MINUTE STRESS BREAK (p 80)

Participants learn a 15-step stretch routine that can be used as a stress break any time of the day. (10 minutes)

92 STOP LOOK AND LISTEN (p 84)

Using a do-it-yourself study guide, trios of participants experiment with techniques to improve listening skills and explore applications of empathy as a stress management strategy. (60 minutes)

93 CENTERING MEDITATION (p 92)

Participants experience the quieting process of meditation and the focusing power of visualization in this guided fantasy. (25-40 minutes)

90 CONFLICT MANAGEMENT

In this thought-provoking learning experience participants explore four conflict-prevention skills and experiment with applying them to specific conflict situations.

GOALS

1) To identify conflict situations that cause stress.

2) To discover and practice alternative approaches for preventing or managing conflict.

GROUP SIZE

Unlimited

TIME FRAME

60 minutes

MATERIALS NEEDED

CONFLICT ALTERNATIVES worksheets for all participants; blackboard or flip chart.

PROCESS

1) The trainer begins by asking participants for examples of conflict and typical conflict situations that they experience (eg, misunderstanding, personality clash, poor performance, difference of opinion or values, lack of cooperation, authority issues, differing goals, competition, etc). As examples are suggested, the trainer records them on the board.

2) After a lengthy and comprehensive list of conflicts has been generated, the trainer introduces the concept of conflict management and describes what participants can expect from this session. Some or all of the following points could be included:

    • It's not what you know, but what you do with what you know that counts in conflict management.

    • This session doesn't promise that you will be able to control conflicts in your life -- after all, people are unpredictable. Nor will taking this course assure that you will win in all conflict situations.

● Managing conflict does not guarantee the outcome,
but it may take away the power of the other person
or the situation to stress you.

3) The trainer notes that most of our attitudes toward
conflict are shaped early in life by the messages we
learn from our environment -- eg, "Button your lip!",
"Turn the other cheek!", "Fighting never solved anything!", etc. Most people learn to dislike, avoid, or
clam up in conflict situations. We believe that it's
wrong, or at least not "nice" to have conflicts.

She goes on to offer an alternative understanding of the
nature of conflict -- that it is natural, inevitable and
desirable -- and challenges participants to begin
changing their attitudes:

● Conflict is an inevitable part of life -- it is
inherent in our differentness -- in people's varying
motivations, backgrounds, perspectives, values,
needs, goals, feelings, expectations, opinions, etc.

● Conflict is desirable because opposition is a way to
think through all the alternatives. Conflict is a
valuable tool to make sure that all major aspects of
important matters are carefully considered.

● The stress of conflict comes when reality doesn't
coincide with our expectations. If we "believe"
(expect) that conflict is unnatural -- then the
reality of conflict is likely to be upsetting!

● To manage conflict successfully, we need to change
our expectations. If we can accept conflict as a
natural part of life, we can free our energy to
focus attention on how to cope with it.

4) The trainer distributes CONFLICT ALTERNATIVES worksheets to participants and asks them to list several
recent conflict situations that they have experienced,
including at least a few that were especially difficult
or are still needing to be resolved. Each conflict is
listed in a separate box at the left of the worksheet.

The trainer explains that the worksheet will be used
during the remainder of the session to record insights
as participants explore four conflict management
strategies that are useful in a wide variety of
settings:
     * Cultivate a positive mental attitude
     * Focus on the issue, not the person
     * Increase your tolerance level
     * Keep conflict in perspective

5) The trainer asks participants to describe how they typically feel in conflict situations such as being called
on the carpet, a family argument or just disagreeing
about what movie to attend.

After several people have given examples (eg, defensive,
scared, anxious, angry, upset, etc) she notes that such
negative feelings often accompany conflict situations,
which is why the first conflict management skill, positive mental attitude is so important.

- Often we perceive conflict as a challenge to our
personal beliefs, opinions, actions, authority.
Even when the conflict is minor we experience an
implied criticism of our own position.

- We usually respond in one of two ways -- we kick
ourselves for being inadequate or we strike out to
protect our position or self-esteem. Neither
response helps resolve the original conflict.

- To deal creatively with conflict, we need to feel
powerful and competent. Instead of generating a
stream of mental put-downs such as, "I failed
again," "I don't measure up," "This is terrible,"
"He's right and I'm wrong," "It's awful to be
caught," etc -- we need to focus on positive
messages such as, "My worth doesn't depend on being
perfect," "I can learn from this," "This is upsetting, but I know how to deal with it," "I have the
same rights as others," "I am valuable and capable,"
"This could be hairy, but I believe in myself," etc.

6) The trainer invites participants to reflect on each of
the conflict situations identified on their CONFLICT
ALTERNATIVES worksheet and decide whether a more
positive mental attitude would be helpful in managing
that particular conflict.

For each situation she asks them to jot down in the
column labelled RAISE SELF-ESTEEM their answers to the
following question:
□ What positive messages could you tell yourself in
the midst of this conflict that would help raise
your self-esteem and therefore your capacity to
resolve the conflict?

7) After most participants have completed the self-esteem
portion of the worksheet, the trainer outlines the
second strategy for managing conflict: focus on the
issue, not the person.

- Conflict is often attributed to negative personality

characteristics or behaviors of people (eg, "I have
a slave-driver for a boss," "She's a lazy typist").

● In fact, most conflicts can be redefined as an <u>issue</u>
resulting from circumstances that affect both parties. This opens the door to resolution because
these circumstances can potentially be changed when
both parties search together for a solution (eg,
"The office is understaffed," "The workload is
erratic," "We need to set priorities," etc).

● Although there are instances when a person's
personality <u>is</u> the problem -- and must be honestly
dealt with -- it is almost always more constructive
to state the conflict as an <u>issue</u> and not attack or
blame the <u>persons</u> involved.

The trainer asks for examples of conflict situations
and demonstrates stating each conflict in both a person-
focused and an issue-focused manner. After modeling one
or two examples, she may ask the group to try redefining
a few more conflicts as person and issue-focused.

8) Once the group seems to understand the process, the
trainer asks participants to look again at their worksheets and apply the issue/person principle to each
situation. To help the participants articulate their
potential use of this skill, she poses the question
below and instructs people to record their answers for
each conflict in the column marked FOCUS ON THE ISSUE.
  □ How could focusing on the issue rather than the
    person be helpful in resolving or preventing this
    conflict?

9) After most people have finished recording their observations, the trainer invites participants to consider the
third strategy for conflict management -- <u>heighten your
tolerance level</u>. She describes the rationale and
process for implementing this approach:

● In general people have unrealistic expectations
about other people. We expect them to act just the
way we want them to -- and we expect them to be
perfect! How outrageous! People are human beings
-- not gods!

● It is impossible to control other people -- even
though we would like to. People will be frustrating, difficult, angry, selfish, incompetent -- no
matter what we prefer. We can prevent or minimize
the stress of conflict if we raise our tolerance
level of other people's behavior! How do we become
more tolerant? The first step is to change the way

we talk to ourselves.

- When faced with a conflict people tend to "awfulize" about the situation, saying things to themselves like, "I can't stand him another minute!" Well, you CAN stand him another minute . . . and you will! Such common self-talk is comical when actually spoken out loud.

The trainer solicits from participants examples of self-talk that reinforces our stance of intolerance (eg, "I'm going to die if this doesn't get decided soon!" "I hate working with her!" "He drives me crazy!"). For each negative statement the group is challenged to suggest more tolerant alternatives (eg, "This person's behavior is frustrating to me. However, I cannot expect her to be perfect -- and she is not likely to change. I better accept it and go on from there!").

10) The trainer invites participants to look over their list of conflicts on their worksheets and apply the increased tolerance level strategy. She instructs people to answer in the column marked INCREASED TOLERANCE the following questions for each conflict:
   □ How might this situation benefit from increased tolerance on my part?
   □ What unrealistic expectations do I have here?
   □ What intolerant messages am I telling myself?
   □ What more tolerant messages could I use instead?

11) The trainer invites participants to consider the final strategy for managing conflict -- keeping it in perspective. She announces that each person has just been awarded $25 which represents the total investment of energy and stress they are currently making in the conflicts listed on their worksheet. Participants are instructed to distribute the $25 among the conflicts according to how much energy or worry they are spending (or usually spend) on each one. These amounts are recorded in the PERSPECTIVE column of the worksheet.

Once everyone has spent their $25 on paper, the trainer asks participants to review their list of conflicts again and reallocate the money, this time based on how much each conflict is really worth. What is its true value and importance in the long run?

The trainer solicits insights and reactions from the group, prompting them with questions such as:
   □ Where are you spending the most? Is the conflict worth it?
   □ What is the relationship between your expenditure and the importance of the conflict?

The trainer concludes by citing the "Law of Creeping Importance":
* If you rate the importance of conflicts on a scale of 1-10, all conflicts will creep up to become 10's.
* The only counterbalance to this law is to be vigilant about keeping conflicts in perspective.

12) The trainer instructs participants to look over the worksheet and choose one conflict situation they would like to work on -- and one of the four management skills/ strategies they would like to practice applying to that situation.

Participants pair up with a neighbor and take turns role playing their conflict situation, experimenting with implementing the new skill.

Note: Adjust the structure, style and length of this role play to your group. One person should begin by explaining his conflict situation and describing the skill he wants to try. His partner can take either role in the conflict. The pairs role play the situation for 2-3 minutes or until the original person is satisfied. He then notes any good ideas generated during the role play before going on to practice the other person's situation.

13) The trainer reconvenes the large group and asks for insights and observations on any aspect of conflict management. In conclusion, she summarizes the key points from the session and encourages participants to continue experimenting with these four strategies in a variety of conflict situations.

VARIATIONS

- The icebreaker, MODELS (p 1), could be adapted for conflict management and included as part of Step 1.

- Step 5 could be spiced up by adding the irrational beliefs BOO-DOWN (Stress 1, p 113)

- If time permits, the roleplays in Step 12 could be expanded by having partners practice all four management strategies.

TRAINER'S NOTES

Submitted by Pat Miller.

CONFLICT MANAGEMENT

CONFLICT SITUATIONS	RAISE SELF-ESTEEM	STAY ISSUE-CENTERED	INCREASE TOLERANCE	KEEP IN PERSPECTIVE

91 EIGHT MINUTE STRESS BREAK

Participants learn a 15-step stretch routine that can be used as a stress break any time of the day.

GOALS

1) To demonstrate the effectiveness of exercise as a stress management technique.

2 To stretch all the major muscle groups.

TIME FRAME

10 minutes

MATERIALS NEEDED

Tape recorder and peppy music.

PROCESS

1) The trainer briefly describes typical benefits of stretching and exercise as stress management techniques:

   • Stretching and vigorous exercise both help discharge accumulated physical tension from the various muscle groups.

   • The increased flow of blood and oxygen to the muscles usually stimulates an increased energy level.

   • Both types of physical activity provide a distraction from emotional or mental strain.

   • Stretching and exercise are effective preventive measures for dealing with stress by systematically letting go of tension before it accumulates to unhealthy proportions. These techniques also are effective in crisis situations to relieve the physical effects of stress.

2) The trainer turns on the music and participants join in as he demonstrates the EIGHT MINUTE STRESS BREAK routine which can easily be incorporated into a busy schedule.

VARIATIONS

■ Choose only a few exercises to teach during this presentation (eg, all the upper body stretches). Then sprinkle the other routines throughout the remainder of the session.

■ To model how this skill could be used in real life, teach the whole sequence at once and then sprinkle repeat performances as mini stretch-breaks at unexpected or particularly stressful moments during the remainder of the learning experience.

■ If the course is several sessions long, go through the sequence once at every meeting in order to entrench the routine in participants' minds.

■ In Step 3 hand out a list of the 14 stretches. Ask people to identify their favorites and make a list of those they especially want to use in the future and the situations where they most need to!

TRAINER'S NOTES

Submitted by Keith Sehnert, MD, author of The Family Doctor's Health Tips (Meadowbrook, 1981), from which this exercise is adapted.

EIGHT MINUTE STRESS BREAK

The 360 Stretch. Begin with your body relaxed, arms and hands
    loose at your sides. Pull your right shoulder up and with
    one smooth movement, bring the shoulder back and around,
    making a complete circle. Repeat this same circular motion
    with the left shoulder. Continue stretching one shoulder,
    then the other, 5 times each. Then reverse the direction,
    using alternate shoulders, five times each. This should
    loosen up your neck, back and shoulders -- places where most
    people store tension.

Starfish Stretch. Begin with your arms stretched overhead,
    slightly bent, eyes turned upward. In a single motion,
    open your hands, spread your fingers wide, and reach up as
    high as you can. Hold that position for a few seconds.
    Then close your fists and lower your arms, with elbows bent.
    Rest a few seconds and then repeat the starfish stretch/rest
    sequence 10-15 times. For variety, stretch to the side.

Snow Angels. Allow your arms to hang loose at your sides. Begin
    to loosen your wrists by shaking your hands, allowing them
    to flop as freely as possible. Continue to shake and flop
    as you slowly raise your arms to the side and up until your
    hands touch overhead. Then allow your arms to gradually
    drop, still shaking and loosening the wrists.

Tall Grass Stalk. Extend your arms out in front of you. While
    concentrating on your shoulders, slowly sweep your hands and
    arms to the side and back, as if pushing tall grass out of
    the way. You should feel a pull along your shoulders and
    arms. Stretch your arms out again and "stalk" for 10 more
    steps.

Bunny Hop. Put your hands on your hips and hop twice on your
    right foot. Now hop twice on your left foot. Continue
    these double hops, alternating feet and adding a side kick
    or a cross kick on the second hop. Continue hopping and
    kicking for 30 seconds, varying your tempo and kick height.

Hoe-Down. Start by getting centered, feet firmly planted, knees
    slightly bent. Lift your right knee up towards your chest,
    slap it with your left hand and then lower your leg and
    stretch it to the side, toes pointing outward. Repeat the
    hoe-down lift 3 more times and then try the left leg for 4
    counts.

Cloud Walk. This is a slow step, rolling from heel to toe, one
    foot at a time, gently stretching the legs and feet. Your
    whole body should be relaxed. Pick up the tempo of the
    heel-toe roll until you reach a slow jog, raising your feet

slightly off the floor at each step. Continue at this pace
for 30 seconds.

Dippity-Do. Start with your legs slightly apart. Dip your body
into an easy kneebend and then spring back to the upright
position. Continue to bend and spring back for 30 seconds,
adding rhythmic arm swings as you increase your pace.

Arch Stretch. With knees slightly bent, join your hands
comfortably behind your back. Slowly arch your back,
letting your hands and stiff arms pull your shoulders and
head down toward the floor. Hold for 5 counts and then
relax, allowing your head to fall forward and your shoulders
curl toward the front. Repeat 7 times.

Twister. With feet shoulder width apart and knees bent, put your
hands on your hips. Keep your back straight as you twist
your shoulders and trunk to the right 3 times and then
return to face forward. Now twist to the opposite side for
3 counts and return to the center. Continue to twist for 8
sets.

Body Bounce. With feet apart, arms at your sides, bend sideways
at the waist, stretching your hand down your leg as you
bounce gently three times to that side. On the fourth count
straighten up. Repeat the stretch and bounce to the other
side. Do 5 body bounces on each side.

Now add your arms to the stretching movement. With your
left arm, reach up and over as you bounce to the right for 3
counts. Repeat to the other side, stretching your right arm
up and over as you bounce to the left 3 counts. Do 5 sets
on each side.

Sneak Peek. Stand straight with your neck, shoulders and back as
relaxed as possible. Tilt your head to the left. Now
slowly roll your head so that your chin falls to your chest
and then comes up as your head tilts to the right. Now look
back over your right shoulder, hold the pose and then relax.
Repeat the stretch, this time starting with your head tilted
to the right and ending with a sneak peek over your left
shoulder. Do four peeks on each side.

The Wave. Stand straight with your arms at your sides, palms
facing out. As you take a long deep breath, slowly (4
counts) raise your arms up over your head. Now, as you
exhale slowly, bring your arms back down, palms facing   (4
downward (4 counts). Repeat this languid wave 6 times.

Hang Loose. Time to shake out your body. Flap your arms, twist
your wrists, shrug your shoulders, jiggle your legs, shake
your feet, flex your knees, bounce your booty until your
whole body feels tingly, loose and relaxed.

92 STOP LOOK AND LISTEN

Using a do-it-yourself study guide, trios of participants
experiment with techniques to improve listening skills and
explore applications of empathy as a stress management
strategy.

GOALS

1) To explore the value of listening as a coping skill in
   stressful situations.

2) To practice listening skills.

GROUP SIZE

Works best with 15 or more people, if there is plenty of
space for small groups to meet separately.

TIME FRAME

60 minutes

MATERIALS NEEDED

Newsprint easel or blackboard; STOP, LOOK AND LISTEN flip
guides for each participant (to be photocopied, cut,
assembled and stapled before the meeting).

PROCESS

*Note: The energizer YOU'RE NOT LISTENING (p 132) makes an
excellent introduction to this exercise.*

*The unusual feature of this listening exercise is the
self-directed booklet that triads of participants use
to work their way through the process. After your
introductory chalktalk, all you as a trainer need to
do is turn people loose, keep time, periodically
announce when to move to the next page, and then sit
back and see what happens!*

1) The trainer introduces the exercise by announcing that
   the next hour or so will be spent in developing an
   unusual but powerful coping skill -- listening.

   She asks the group for ideas on why listening might be a
   useful skill for managing stress, and lists the suggestions on the blackboard or newsprint. As people contribute, she weaves their responses into a brief chalktalk
   on communication, stress and listening:

- Most people are good listeners when they want to be, but many simply don't choose to use this skill as frequently as they might -- especially in stressful situations.

- Breakdown in communication is a common cause of stress. Misunderstandings, misinterpretations, hidden agendas, unresolved conflicts, disagreements, often trigger our stress response.

- One way to handle such breakdowns and unstress ourselves in the process is to respond with empathy rather than anger or defensiveness. This response forces us to acknowledge the other person's point of view which broadens our perspective at the same time it affirms the other's experience.

2) The trainer briefly describes empathy and the STOP, LOOK AND LISTEN paradigm.

- Empathy is a special kind of listening that literally means to "feel in", or to stand in another's shoes for a moment -- to get inside that person's experience, to soak it up, and try to view it from his or her perspective.

- This is not a passive process. Being a good listener means more than just allowing the other person to talk -- although that's a good start. Empathy involves a three step process -- stop, look and listen.

- Stop. Stop talking. Stop competing for attention. Stop worrying about your own feelings. Be quiet. Put aside your judgments and expectations about the person or the topic. Try to approach this with an open mind. Stop and take a deep breath. As you exhale, let go of your own agenda. Choose to focus on the other person.

- Look. Look at the other person, eyeball to eyeball. Pay attention. Show your interest. Get involved. Notice verbals and non-verbals. Observe, but don't interpret. Explore, don't judge. Look for this person's unique viewpoint. Put on his or her glasses and look at the world through those lenses.

- Listen. Listen to what this person says. Listen to the words. Listen to the body language. Listen to the meanings behind the message. Listen to the feelings. Listen to the silence. Reflect on what you've heard. Now respond -- let the other person know what you've heard. Paraphrase. Comment on

© 1986   Whole Person Press   PO Box 3151   Duluth MN 55803

what you noticed -- without interpreting. Feed back
your perceptions and check them out (eg, "Is this
what you meant? thought? felt?"). If they're
wrong, reach out and try again to understand.

3) The trainer divides participants into groups of three
    people each, and instructs them to decide -- for the
    purpose of this exercise -- who will be "A", who will be
    "B", and who "C". While groups are deciding, she
    distributes a copy of the STOP, LOOK AND LISTEN flip
    guide to all participants, requesting that they not look
    at the booklet until directed.

4) The trainer outlines the process of the exercise:

    * Most of the remaining time will be spent in these
      trios, completing the process described in these do-
      it-yourself flip guides. You will practice the
      skill of listening to each other by dialoguing about
      various topics assigned by the flip guides.

    * In most of the 5-10 minute segments, two people in
      the trio will dialogue while the other remains
      silent -- observing the listening process. These
      roles switch for each segment.

    * The flip guide gives complete instructions, includ-
      ing the questions to be discussed and the roles to
      be taken by each person. When there is more than
      one question on a page, the two people "in dialogue"
      take turns listening to each other's answers to one
      question before moving on to the next.

    * While dialoguing, you are to listen intently to each
      other and try to fully understand what the other is
      saying. This will take time -- and you may not be
      able to answer all the questions in the time allot-
      ted. That's great! The purpose is to listen to
      each other, not to race through to the end!

    * I will keep time. Follow the instructions in the
      booklet and unless it specifically says to turn to
      the next page, wait for my signal before moving on.

5) The trainer instructs participants to introduce them-
    selves and look at the first three pages of the flip
    guide, which are a self-paced introduction. She reminds
    everyone to follow the directions in the guide and that
    she will keep track of time and announce when to move
    on. (5-6 minutes)

    *Note: You may want to use a bell, harmonica or whistle
           to indicate the time. Be sure you are familiar*

with the timetable and instructions on each flip guide page so that you can keep time correctly and answer any questions. When you announce the time, you may want to remind people to use their empathic skills -- eg, "Remember to paraphrase and check out your perceptions!" or "Take your time -- listen with empathy!" etc.

6) When the last page is finished, the trainer asks the sextets to spend 3 more minutes brainstorming a list of stressful situations where empathy would be an effective stress management strategy.

7) The trainer reconvenes the entire group and asks for insights and observations about the experience of listening and the value of listening as a coping skill. After several people have shared, she solicits examples of situations where the skill might be useful, listing them on the board and using the data generated to summarize learnings from the session.

8) In closing, the trainer issues a final challenge:

I can teach you the skill of listening, but I can't decide for you when you will use it. It's your choice when you implement it. Practice it so you'll be ready! Then choose to use it in some unlikely situations -- and see what happens!

VARIATIONS

■ If time is limited, some of the listening processes from the flip guides may be shortened or skipped entirely. Be aware, however, that when the process is shortened the intensity and benefit of the experience will also be lessened.

TRAINER'S NOTES

STOP, LOOK AND LISTEN
dialogue instructions

READ THIS SECTION SILENTLY. DO NOT LOOK AHEAD IN THIS BOOKLET.

When we're under pressure, one of the first things that is likely
to buckle is our ability to listen. Too bad! Empathy -- the
process of active, care-full listening -- is one of the best
stress management techniques available.

This exercise is designed to help you and your partners explore
the value of listening when under stress. So, during the next
hour, give yourself permission to STOP, LOOK and LISTEN:

> STOP -   Take a deep breath, exhale and get ready to pay
>   attention.
>
> LOOK -   Put on your partner's perceptual glasses and try
>   to see his or her viewpoint rather than
>   concentrating on your own.
>
> LISTEN - Tune in to the meaning behind the words, the
>   person behind the pitter patter.

(go on to the next page)

2

1) All information shared here is strictly confidential.

2) You will be engaging in a series of conversations,
    alternating roles as observer, sharer and listener. Follow
    the instructions and take turns as indicated -- both partners
    respond to each question before moving on.

3) When it is your turn to speak, respond to the questions at
    whatever level of disclosure feels comfortable. You may also
    decline to answer any question.

5) When you are listening, be sure to practice all the empathic
    skills:

> show interest - eye contact, nods, uh-huhs
> reach out - to pick up the verbal/non-verbal message
> focus on partner - set aside your own agenda
> respond - summarize, check your perceptions

6) When you are observing, pay attention to the process and
    impact of listening. At the end of the hour you will have a
    chance to share your insights.

(check to make sure everyone understands, then turn the page)

© 1986 Whole Person Press   PO Box 3151   Duluth MN 55803

3

A observes
B and C dialogue   *(5 minutes)*
B shares first

One stress I've experienced today is . . .

> *B shares first.*
> *C responds empathically -- pause to digest the answer,*
> *reflect on it and paraphrase what your partner has*
> *said. Ask if your perception is accurate. If so,*
> *then switch roles and give your answer to the question.*
> *If not, try again.*
> *A observes only.*

I coped with it by . . .

> *(same process and order as above)*

When I'm under a lot of stress, my body lets me know by . .

> *(same process and order as above)*

(wait for instructions)

4

B observes
A and C dialogue   *(5 minutes)*
C shares first

Tell your partner about an instance when someone listened
empathically and whole-heartedly to you. What do you remember
about how it felt?

> *C answers first while A listens empathically.*
> *Then C listens while A answers the question.*

When do you especially want to be listened to and heard?

> *(same process as above)*

(the trainer will tell you when to go on)

5

C observes
A and B dialogue   *(10 minutes)*
A shares first

Situations where I find it hard to listen . . .

People I have trouble listening to . . .

Describe a recent situation when you had difficulty listening or
didn't want to listen (eg, argument, criticism, assignment,
challenge, request, instruction, angry outburst, whining).

> What did you want to hear?
> What did you hear at the time?
> In retrospect, what did the person really want to
> communicate?

                   (wait for the signal to move ahead)

6

A observes
B and C dialogue   *(5 minutes each, 10 minutes total)*
C shares first

Practice supportive listening by paraphrasing and responding with
understanding. Take your time!

SHARER: Describe a situation at home or work that upsets you.

LISTENER: Listen and respond empathically. Show interest. Try
     to get inside your partner's shoes and understand the situa-
     tion from his/ her perspective.

     Don't give advice. Don't make judgments -- not even
     positive ones. Don't ask questions that would throw your
     partner off. Don't problem-solve or reassure.

     Do reach out for the feelings and meanings behind the words.
     Do summarize what you've heard and check out your percep-
     tions -- if they are inaccurate, try again until you've
     heard fully.

                   (wait for the signal to move ahead)

7

C observes
A and B dialogue   *(5 minutes)*
B shares first

Paraphrase techniques also work in conflict situations!

With your partner find a subject on which you disagree (eg, age
for toilet training, religious doctrine, men with pierced ears,
nuclear disarmament, politics, best brand of detergent, who will
win the Super Bowl, etc).

Dialogue about this topic for 5 minutes, using the following
paraphrase rule:

>   Each of you must restate your partner's position to his or
>   her satisfaction before you can air your own views.

Use this rule throughout the discussion. If your viewpoint has
not been heard, ask your partner to listen again until you really
feel your partner understands your position. When listening,
remember to suspend your judgment and biases -- stay open to
hearing the other person's perspective.

                    (wait for the signal to go on)

                                                                  8

STOP   Take a deep breath.

LOOK   Around the room and find another trio you'd like to talk
         with. Join with them to make a sextet.

LISTEN   To each other as you take 5 minutes to share insights
         and reactions to this experience.

              * As observers, what did you notice about listening?
              * How did it feel to be heard?
              * How accurately did your partner listen and
                understand?
              * How difficult was it to listen? When?
              * Was there any difference in empathy with a
                supportive versus a conflict situation?
              * Were there any surprises?
              * This was a stressful situation. How did listening
                work as a coper for you?

                    (wait for further instructions)

93 CENTERING MEDITATION

Participants experience the quieting process of meditation
and the focusing power of visualization in this guided
fantasy.

GOALS

1) To learn the principles of meditation and imagery as
   skills for relaxation.

2) To experience quiet, calm, peace and a sense of inner
   vision.

GROUP SIZE

Unlimited

TIME FRAME

25-40 minutes

MATERIALS NEEDED

Blank paper for all; soothing soft music.

PROCESS

1) The trainer introduces the exercise by describing the
   importance of relaxation as an antidote to stress --
   both as a remedy and as a preventive measure.

2) The trainer notes that this skill building experience
   uses elements of two powerful techniques for inducing a
   relaxed state. He goes on to describe the process and
   power of meditation and guided imagery:

   ● Meditation may be the most wholistic of all stress
     management skills since it involves sensory aware-
     ness, physical relaxation, surrender of thought
     processes and focusing on the "life force" through
     breathing and contemplation.

   ● The key elements needed for effective meditation
     include: (1) a quiet environment that's free from
     distraction; (2) a comfortable position that can be
     maintained easily for 20 minutes; (3) a phrase,
     sound or object to focus on so that distracting
     thoughts will pass; and (4) an open and passive
     attitude, accepting whatever the experience brings.

- Scientists have discovered that the <u>hypothalmus</u> (the area of the brain that gathers information input from the senses) responds to <u>symbolic</u> stimuli almost as well as to the real thing. Just as a terrifying movie can provoke our stress reaction, visualizing a peaceful scene will calm our bodies down!

  With practice, we can learn to trigger the relaxation response almost instantly just by using our imaginations!

3) The trainer invites participants to join in the centering meditation and describes the activity:

   * *This relaxation routine combines breathing, <u>visual imagery</u> and some aspects of <u>meditation</u> in a process of physical and mental centering.*

   * *The first part consists of a quieting process to get our energy centered. We will then take an imaginary walk in the forest. The last step involves some writing. Everyone will need to have paper and pencil handy so as not to disrupt the mood.*

4) The trainer instructs participants to relax in their chairs and close their eyes. He turns on the soft music he has selected and slowly reads the CENTERING MEDITATION script.

   Note: Be sure to read the script very slowly. To pace yourself, take a deep breath at every (. . .) and pause between sections. Leave the music playing softly in the background while participants write down their conversations.

5) After he has completed reading the script, the trainer allows several minutes (3-10) for people to write their dialogues. He then asks participants to complete the portion they are working on and return their attention to the group.

6) Finally, the trainer invites any who are willing to read their dialogues aloud to the entire group.

   Note: Reading these dialogues aloud can be an extremely powerful process. Be patient and wait for volunteers. Do not let people talk about or explain their dialogues. Ask them to read what they have written without additional comment. Do not comment or permit discussion. Simply listen to the dialogue, thank the sharer and move to the next. When all who wish to read their dialogues have done so, this exercise is concluded.

CENTERING MEDITATION

We are sitting in quiet . . . and calm . . .
Letting the core become clear . . .
Letting the thoughts slow their pace . . .
Letting the breath become regular and slow . . .
Letting the self become still . . .

We are sitting in quiet . . . and calm . . .
Letting the breath become steady and deep . . .
Letting energies that were once chasing madly
focus inward and rest . . .
within the stillness of our center . . .
Letting energies come to rest
upon the steady rhythm of our breathing . . .

Breathing at the center, our breath becomes deeper . . .
Breathing at the quiet and calm of our core
our breath becomes pure and clear . . .

Our breathing is free . . . and regular . . .
Our breathing finds it easy to come . . . and go . . .
on its own . . . without our effort . . .

Our thoughts become quiet . . .
Wandering thoughts come to rest . . .
Our feelings become one . . . one flow of experience . . .
All rests on the regular rhythm of our steady breathing . . .
that moves into our soul . . .
Bringing peace . . . and quiet . . .
Bringing healing to our core . . .

We are centered . . . we are quiet. . .
All parts connected . . .
Connected together . . .
by the rhythm of our steady breathing . . .

We are clear . . . and we know clearly . . . and deeply . . .
We know peace . . .
As breathing moves . . . in . . . and out . . .
at the center of our being . . .
The core . . . waits calmly . . .
for the quiet . . . of the breathing . . . .
to bring it healing life . . .

I am aware of seeing beyond my eyes . . .
of hearing with more than my ears . . .
of knowing outside of my mind . . .
I see and know truth at the core of my being . . .
And I wait . . . and watch . . . in quiet . . . and calm . . .
Aware only of my steady, regular breathing . . .

As I wait . . . I find myself in a forest . . .

A forest of trees spread far apart with large trunks . . .
The trees are so tall they soar above me . . .
The huge canopy of branches overlapping as a ceiling to cover me
and block out the bright sunlight . . .

The sun shining so brightly above . . .
cannot get through to the forest floor where I stand . . .
Where I walk it is dark . . .
Where I walk on the floor of the forest . . . it is quiet . . .

The quiet surrounds me . . . as I listen to the stillness . . .
The silence follows me . . .
as I move slowly through the forest.

I listen to the presence around me . . .
I feel the power of the quiet that surrounds me . . .
And I know I am no longer alone . . .

As I watch . . . I notice a small bush . . .
It is unlike anything else in the forest . . .
It is glowing . . . gently . . .
Its glowing lights up the darkness of the forest
As it hovers . . . barely touching the ground . . .

It glows before me . . .
Its flowers twinkle with a special light
and its glowing is strong . . . and even . . .
Showing no signs of diminishing . . .
Showing no source of power . . .
The bush glows . . .
with a soft brightness . . . that comes from within . . .

I am standing deep in the forest . . .
It is dark at the floor of the forest . . .
But I am touched . . . and surrounded by a soft light
that comes from the bush . . .
It reaches me . . . touches me . . . gently . . .

I feel the soft quality of being that comes from its light . . .
I am touched by a gentle power that comes from beyond me . . .
I am touched by a power that does not diminish . . .
The glowing bush is part of me . . .
It glows within me . . .
It enters my heart . . . and burns steadily . . .

The glowing bush in the woods bathes me with its soft light . . .
The bush will stay with me . . .

The glowing bush enlightens my core
at the very center of my being . . .
where my breathing maintains its regular steady rhythm . . .
At this center of my being the bush lights my heart . . .
and shows me truth . . .

As I stand before the bush my center is quiet . . .
and calm . . . . My center is light . . .

As I stand before it . . .
I become aware I am no longer alone . . .
A wise and kind person is with me . . . one whom I trust . . .
A wise person . . . very gentle and caring . . .
In the quiet . . . the wise one speaks to me . . .
Speaks about the bush . . . about life . . . about me . . .
And I listen . . .

And I respond . . .

And the wise one speaks . . . and I listen . . .
And respond . . .

Speaking . . . and listening . . .

Listening . . . and speaking . . .

As our dialogue continues . . .
I experience the growing of wisdom in me . . .
Wisdom . . . from my friend . . . from the bush . . .
from within me . . .
A clarity and knowledge of truth grows in me . . .

Listening . . . and speaking . . . speaking and listening . . .
I am being touched . . .

(pause)

As you are ready . . .
slowly come back into the room,
just enough to make some notes of the dialogue . . .
between you and your wise friend . . .

Write it like a play with your friend speaking first . . .
and then write your response . . .

(pause 20 to 30 seconds)

As you are ready . . .
slowly come back into the room
just enough to make some notes of the dialogue
between you and your wise friend . . .
Write it like a play with your friend speaking first
and then write your response . . .

(Pause 3 to 10 minutes while people write)

Take just a minute now
to finish up whatever you're working on . . .
Then return you attention to this room . . .

ACTION PLANNING/CLOSURE

94 CLOSING FORMATION (p 97)

In this round-robin ending participants pair up with many different partners to briefly share reactions, insights and coping plans. (10-30 minutes)

95 EXIT INTERVIEW (p 100)

In dyads participants review course content and publicly affirm their plans for improved stress management. (20-30 minutes)

96 RECIPE FOR SUCCESS WITH STRESS (p 104)

Participants reflect on the ingredients for successful stress management as they cook up innovative personal recipes for handling stress. (25-30 minutes)

97 MY STRESS REDUCTION PROGRAM (p 107)

This step-by-step planning process helps participants formulate a specific plan for managing a stress-related problem. (20-30 minutes)

98 CHANGE PENTAGON (p 110)

Participants explore each aspect of life (mental, physical, interpersonal, spiritual and lifestyle) seeking positive alternatives for managing stress. They then draw up a "whole person" plan for dealing with specific problem situations. (15-30 minutes)

94 CLOSING FORMATION

In this round-robin ending participants pair up with many
different partners to briefly share reactions, insights and
coping plans.

GOALS

1) To review highlights of the learning experience.

2) To touch base with many other participants before
   ending the session/course.

3) To solidify specific plans for better stress
   management.

GROUP SIZE

Works best with 16 or more people, but can be adapted for
smaller groups.

TIME FRAME

10-30 minutes.

PROCESS

1) <u>Twos</u>. The trainer asks participants to stand up and
   quickly find a partner -- perhaps the person in an
   adjacent seat. As soon as everyone is paired, she asks
   them to spend 1 minute brainstorming together, identifying the most important points covered during the
   course/session.

2) <u>Fours</u>. Pairs are instructed to find another pair and
   join together as a foursome. As soon as the groups
   have gathered, the trainer announces that they will
   have 2 minutes to talk about the most exciting ideas/
   concepts/attitudes/skills they have learned. Each
   person should get a chance to share his favorite.

.3) <u>Eights</u>. The trainer calls time and explains the next
   formation:

```
            B          Each foursome will choose another
            A          quartet and form a double circle, one
     B A    A B        group back to back in the middle (A's)
            A          and the other group on the outside,
            B          facing the center (B's).  People in the
                       outside group (B's) position themselves
                       so that everyone is facing a partner in
                       the inside group (see diagram).
```

*Note: If the group does not divide evenly into eights,
see suggestions under VARIATIONS.*

4) The trainer chooses a sentence stub from the CLOSING
FORMATION PROMPTS and reads it to the group,
instructing participants to share with their partners
the first response that comes to mind.

After 1 minute, the trainer calls time and directs all
the people in outside groups (B's) to shift one person
to the right, finding a new partner. She chooses
another sentence stub and asks participants to share
their "off the top of the head" responses.

This process is repeated two more times, using
different prompts. By now all the A's in one formation
have shared with all the B's.

5) The trainer asks all the A's in the room to stay put
where they are, while each outside group of B's moves on
to a new group of A's, making a new formation.

*Note: This can be a chaotic process with a large group.
Help them out by deciding which group of B's
should go where (eg, move to the next group --
to your left, toward the windows, or counter
clockwise, etc), and directing them verbally and
non-verbally.*

Step 4 is repeated in the new formation, rotating
partners and using a new sentence stub for each new
partner.

6) The trainer invites participants to return to their
seats and solicits observations and insights from the
group before making her own closing remarks.

7) In conclusion the trainer may ask people to write a
summary of the ideas and personal resolutions that they
want to remember and take home from this experience.

VARIATION

■ If the group does not divide evenly into 8's, the process
can be adapted to groups of 3 and 6, or after Step 1 pairs
could line up (as for a Virginia reel). One line stays
stationery while the other moves one person to the right
after each prompt/response sequence. Continue until the
group seems to be tiring.

CLOSING FORMATION PROMPTS

One thing I learned about myself in this course is . . .

I am still confused about . . .

The part of this experience I liked best is . . .

One thing I particularly liked about the trainer/leader is . . .

One thing I will tell other people about this experience is . .

Something I've noticed about your coping style is . . .

One thing I appreciate about myself as a participant is . . .

One personal resolution I've made is . . .

The most surprising thing I've discovered here is . . .

The most disturbing insight I've had is . . .

One way I've learned I'm like most other people here is . . .

One way I've learned I'm unique from others here is . . .

One situation where I know I need to use what I've learned . . .

One personal discovery I've made is . . .

The best way to manage stress is . . .

The person in my environment who will benefit most from what I've learned is . . .

95 EXIT INTERVIEW

In dyads participants review course content and publicly affirm their plans for improved stress management.

GOALS

1) To reinforce concepts and techniques presented during the learning experience.

2) To provide closure.

3) To articulate plans for integrating and implementing stress management principles in daily life.

GROUP SIZE

Unlimited as long as there is space for pairs to find privacy.

TIME FRAME

20-30 minutes; longer with a large group.

MATERIALS NEEDED

TED KOPPEL and BARBARA WALTERS INTERVIEW OUTLINES for each dyad.

PROCESS

1) The trainer instructs participants to find a partner with whom to share this closing experience.

   Note: If participants have stayed in the same small group during the learning experience, encourage them to choose someone outside that group as a partner. This facilitates transition and reentry to the "real world."

2) After everyone is settled, the trainer explains that partners will be interviewing each other about what they have learned during the course and how they hope to apply it in real life situations.

   Pairs decide who will be Ted Koppel and who will be Barbara Walters. The trainer distributes TED KOPPEL and BARBARA WALTERS INTERVIEW OUTLINES to the appropriate person in each dyad.

Participants are instructed to alternate asking questions. "Barbara Walters" asks the first question from her outline and makes brief notes of her partner's response. Then "Ted Koppel" asks the first question from his outline and notes his partner's response. "Barbara" goes next with her second question, and then "Ted" asks his second. This process continues until all questions have been posed and answered. The whole sequence should take about 15 minutes.

Note: Remind people that understanding what their partner is saying is much more important than getting all the words down. A quick review of good listening skills (attending behavior, paraphrase, open-ended questions, etc) might be helpful.

After about 10 minutes the trainer announces that there are 5 minutes left. Some pairs may need to speed up the process to get to the final questions. Others who finish early may want to go back and explore some questions in more depth.

3) The trainer calls time and asks participants to spend 3 minutes writing a few sentences briefly summarizing the highlights shared by the person they interviewed.

4) In closing, participants read these summaries out loud to the whole group. The trainer acknowledges each contribution and closes with an affirmation of the exciting growth and learning they have shared together.

Partners are encouraged to exchange interview papers to take home as souvenirs and reminders of their insights and resolutions for change.

TRAINER'S NOTES

BARBARA WALTERS
INTERVIEW OUTLINE

A. Let's talk for a moment about the most interesting,
    surprising aspects of your learning experience. What really
    caught your attention?

B. Speaking personally, based on your history with the issue of
    stress, which specific coping methods do you think would be
    most helpful for you to learn? . . . And how do you think
    this would help you avoid some of the troublesome spots
    you've gotten yourself into in the past?

C. I know that you have a reputation for keeping your plans
    secret, but won't you please give us a glimpse of the
    personal management plan for stress you hammered out during
    this session?

D. As you well know, sabotage of our own good intentions is the
    most prevalent force preventing positive change in people.
    How are you most likely to sabotage your new plans for
    managing stress? . . . And what steps have you taken to
    prevent yourself from sabotaging your own good intentions?

SUMMARY

TED KOPPEL
INTERVIEW OUTLINE

A. Would you focus for a moment on some of the most meaningful
    and helpful learnings you gained from this course? What
    will you take home? What strikes you as most significant?

B. Would you explain clearly for our viewers at home the
    aspect of stress management you believe is most difficult to
    understand and to put into practice?

C. Some would say that while stress courses provide an elixir
    to help people feel good, that in the end these courses
    don't ever do much good -- because, these same critics point
    out, people never really change their bad habits. In the
    light of your recent training what would you say to these
    allegations? . . . And specifically, what changes, if any,
    are you prepared to make on the basis of your learning here?

D. Now that you have this course under your belt, what do you
    need to do next? How are you planning to accomplish this?

SUMMARY

96 RECIPE FOR SUCCESS WITH STRESS

Participants reflect on the ingredients for successful stress management as they cook up innovative personal recipes for handling stress.

GOALS

1) To review qualities that are particularly effective in coping with stress.

2) To promote creativity, humor and self-expression.

GROUP SIZE

Unlimited

TIME FRAME

25-30 minutes

MATERIALS NEEDED

RECIPE FOR SUCCESS WITH STRESS forms for all participants.

PROCESS

1) The trainer announces that this closing exercise will give everyone a chance to play the role of expert by creating a secret recipe for success with stress. He distributes RECIPE FOR SUCCESS WITH STRESS forms to all, explaining that participants can make up whatever ingredients, proportions and directions they believe would make a good stress manager. When finished, the description should take the form of a cookbook recipe.

Note: Before using this exercise with a group, create two or three sample recipes of your own that will serve as examples. (eg, "Take one harried Type A person, add two tons of patience and a dollop of humor, mix vigorously and set in the sun to rest for 3 days. Then massage vigorously, stir in a gallon of values clarification, a pound of faith and a pinch of play. Sprinkle with forgiveness and let it breathe!")

To help the group get going, you may want to generate lists of typical as well as serious measurements (cups, oodles, a scant teaspoon) and directions (combine, toss together, pour in, cool off). Encourage people to think seriously about

> *what they've learned about coping with stress and*
> *then to be as imaginative, creative, and zany as*
> *they can in writing their recipe for success.*

2) One by one, participants read their recipes to the
    group.

3) The trainer summarizes the characteristics included in
    the recipes and uses them as a springboard to review
    positive strategies for managing stress.

VARIATIONS

■ Recipes could be collected, duplicated and compiled in a
   cookbook for distribution to all participants. This serves
   as a good follow-up reminder of the learning experience.

■ If the group is larger than 20 people and time is limited,
   participants could form smaller groups (10-16 people) for
   sharing recipes.

■ Recipes could be written for specific situations such as
   "success with managing change" or "handling conflict" or
   "being assertive" or "dealing with difficult people."

TRAINER'S NOTES

Submitted by Mark Warner.

* *

Recipe for _____Success With Stress_____

From the kitchen of _____

* *

97 MY STRESS REDUCTION PROGRAM

This step-by-step planning process helps participants formulate a specific plan for managing a stress-related problem.

GOALS

1) To practice a process for developing a stress management program tailored to deal with specific stressors.

2) To elicit personal commitment to change.

TIME FRAME

20-30 minutes

MATERIALS NEEDED

MY STRESS REDUCTION PROGRAM worksheets for all.

PROCESS

1) Participants are invited to reflect privately on the sources of stress in their lives and to make a list of specific stressors and/or stressful patterns they would like to change.

   Note: To prime the pump give several examples of a wide range of stressors, including some that partici- pants have mentioned earlier in the learning experience (eg, overeating, financial instability, hassles with the baby-sitter, death in the family, illness, poor self-image, noisy office, etc).

2) The trainer distributes MY STRESS REDUCTION PROGRAM worksheets and asks everyone to choose one stress-maker to focus on for the remainder of the exercise.

   In answering the first question on the worksheet, parti- cipants are instructed to describe the stressor briefly. The trainer then guides the group through the rest of the planning process, giving examples as needed and adjusting the pace to the rhythm of the group.

3) The trainer asks participants to share examples of their personal stress reduction programs and closes by reminding everyone that this same process can be used to develop a strategy for any stressor.

Submitted by Jim Cathcart.

© 1986   Whole Person Press   PO Box 3151   Duluth MN 55803

MY STRESS REDUCTION PROGRAM

(example)

    1) This is the problem:

*(not getting
enough exercise)*

    2) This is what I can do about it:

*(change my schedule
to exercise 3 hours
per week)*

    3) This is what I'm doing now that needs to be changed.

*(when I come home,
I get a drink
and sit down)*

    4) This is what I could do instead:

*(play racqetball
at noon; take bus
to work; join
health club and
work out at night)*

    5) This is what I will do:

*(take a brisk
walk instead of
a cocktail)*

6)   This is my goal:

*(four weeks from
today I'll be able
to walk easily
for 30 minutes
after work)*

7)   This is how I'll reward myself when I reach my goal:

*(buy new stereo
speakers)*

8) This is how I'll work my plan: (how often? where? when?)

*(Every day after
work I'll walk to
the park 3 miles
from home.   I
won't have a drink
after work,
starting today.)*

9)   This is the result(s) that I expect:

*(reduced alcohol
consumption,
increased
aerobic capacity)*

10)   This is how I'll evaluate my progress:

*(pulse checks,
logging mileage,
daily weigh-in,
recording
alcohol intake)*

98 CHANGE PENTAGON

Participants explore each aspect of life (mental, physical, interpersonal, spiritual and lifestyle) seeking positive alternatives for managing stress. They then draw up a "whole person" plan for dealing with specific problem situations.

GOALS

1) To isolate stressful situations that require attention.

2) To expand awareness of coping options in each dimension of life that might reduce stress.

3) To make a plan for coping in a new way with a stressful situation.

GROUP SIZE

Unlimited; works well with individuals, too.

TIME FRAME

15-30 minutes

MATERIALS NEEDED

Several CHANGE PENTAGON worksheets for each participant.

PROCESS

1) The trainer asks participants to mentally review the issues that have come up for them during the learning experience and to identify several stress-provoking situations or patterns that they would like to alter.

   He distributes several CHANGE PENTAGON worksheets to each participant, instructing them to write a different stress-provoking situation in the center circle of each sheet.

2) Participants choose one situation on which to focus. The trainer talks them through the process of investigating each of the five life areas for changes they could make that might help them manage this particular stress-provoking pattern or situation more effectively.

   To help participants generate ideas, the trainer asks facilitative questions for each area:

       □ physical changes -- any alterations in exercise? diet? environment? sleep? routine? pace? relaxation?

       □ thinking/feeling changes -- what different ideas or perceptions might be helpful? what about changes in attitudes? opinions? feelings?

       □ changes in relationships -- friends? family? communication patterns? conflict resolution?

       □ spiritual changes -- what alterations in faith? values? meditation/prayer life?

       □ lifestyle changes -- what changes in focus and commitments? daily, weekly, yearly patterns? life work satisfaction? long and short-term goals? community service?

4) Participants repeat the process with one or more additional stress-provoking situations. The trainer invites participants to join two other people and brainstorm together about additional changes that they might make in the different areas of life to manage their stress-provokers better.

5) Participants are invited to review all the suggestions for positive change they have listed for each different stress-provoking situation. At the bottom of each worksheet people select the changes they want to make and write a personal plan of action to deal with that particular stress.

6) The trainer invites those participants who wish to read their plans out loud to the group.

TRAINER'S NOTES

CHANGE PENTAGON

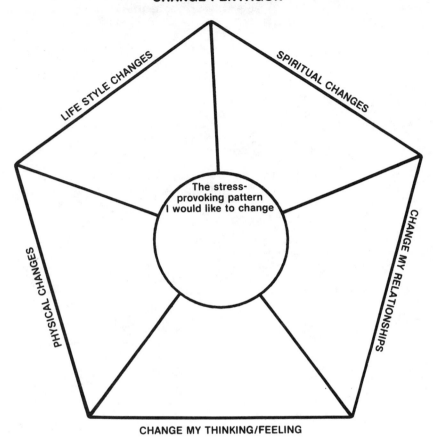

MY PLAN OF ACTION:

GROUP ENERGIZERS

99 KICKING YOUR STRESS HABITS CAN-CAN (p 113)

Participants kick up their heels as they symbolically kick sources of stress out of their lives.

100 CHINESE SWING (p 114)

In this invigorating exercise break participants learn an ancient oriental technique for releasing stress.

101 CLOUDS TO SUNSHINE (p 116)

This adaptation of a traditional T'ai Chi exercise allows participants to breathe and stretch easily while imagining four different scenes from nature.

102 DO-IT-YOURSELF SINGALONG (p 118)

Participants compose stress and coping lyrics for familiar melodies.

103 GROANS AND MOANS (p 120)

In this noisy energizer participants experiment with an old-fashioned remedy for stress.

104 TUG OF WAR (p 122)

In this game of strategy, participants pair up to explore alternative approaches to conflict.

105 WARM HANDS (p 124)

Participants imagine their way to warm hands and a profound sense of relaxation.

106 WHAT'S THE HURRY? (p 126)

This touching parable points out how striving too hard to reach a goal may have stressful side effects.

107 YOU'RE NOT LISTENING (p 129)

Partners work hard at "not listening" to each other and then brainstorm essentials of good listening.

108 PUSHING MY BUTTONS (p 131)

In this self-care break participants stimulate accupressure points to get their energy flowing again.

99 KICKING YOUR STRESS CAN-CAN

In this invigorating dance routine participants kick up
their heels as they symbolically kick sources of stress out
of their lives.

GOALS

1) To demonstrate exercise as a pleasurable and effective
    stress-reducer.

2) To target specific stressors for change.

TIME FRAME

5 minutes or longer

MATERIALS NEEDED

Can-can (Offenbach's "Orpheus in the Underworld," Andre
Previn's "Gaite Parisienne") or other lively dance music.

PROCESS

1) The trainer invites participants to think of several
    stressful situations, people, attitudes, events, etc
    that they would like to "kick out" of their life right
    now. (Or consult a list of stressors generated earlier
    in the learning experience.)

2) The trainer asks everyone to get up and move around in
    the room so that all have plenty of space to dance and
    kick.

    *Note: If the room is fairly crowded, have people form
        lines, shoulder to shoulder, to maximize space.*

3) The trainer demonstrates the can-can step:

    * hop on left foot, bringing right knee up to chest;
    * hop on left foot, tapping right on the floor;
    * hop on left foot, kicking right foot out front;
    * hop on left foot, tapping right on floor;
        * repeat this sequence 4 times;

    * change to hopping on right foot, kicking left;
        * repeat 4 times then alternate to other foot.

4) The trainer starts the music and invites participants to
    dance, visualizing that with every kick they are booting
    a troublesome stressor out of their life.

100 CHINESE SWING

In this invigorating exercise break participants learn an ancient oriental technique for releasing stress.

GOALS

1) To stimulate energy flow in the body and to promote deep breathing.

2) To discharge muscular tension.

GROUP SIZE

Unlimited as long as there is space for all to swing their arms without obstruction.

TIME FRAME

10 minutes

PROCESS

1) The trainer introduces THE SWING, summarizing the following points:

- This is an ancient Chinese exercise which seems to have a power similar to accupressure for generating "energy" or "chi", particularly in the lower body organs.

- The SWING is especially good for people who work in offices since when we are sitting, all the organs below the lungs are pressed together and the energy cannot circulate well in the lower trunk and legs.

- Proponents of the SWING claim that this exercise can lead to improvement in general muscle tone and digestive functioning, increased circulatory efficiency and relief of mental and physical tensions.

    Note: You might joke, "Well, even if it doesn't give us all of those benefits, at least this exercise will get us up and moving, and give us an enjoyable break. Who knows -- some of you may even be instantly healed by this powerful tool!"

2) Participants are invited to stand and spread out around the room so that everyone is free to swing their arms forward and backward without bumping anything.

The trainer demonstrates as he describes the stance and the swing technique:

* *Stand with your feet apart, at shoulder width.*

* *Let your arms hang loosely at your sides, palms facing backward.*

* *Hold the belly in and the upper body erect; relax your neck by lowering it forward.*

* *Grasp the floor with toes and heels and tighten the muscles of your legs and thighs so that you feel most of your weight centered in the lower part of your body.*

* *Focus your eyes on a selected point at least ten feet away, and relax your mind.*

* *To start, force your arms backward as far as possible. Then let them swing freely forward by the force of gravity until they reach a natural position at about a 60-degree angle in front of your body.*

3) As soon as everyone catches on, the trainer asks people to start counting their swings and keep on until they reach 100-150 repetitions, paying particular attention to any bodily sensations that they experience.

4) When almost all are finished, the trainer solicits reactions from the group.
   □ What sensations did you experience?
   □ Do they feel energized or fatigued?
   □ What happened to your tension level?

5) In closing, the trainer describes the recommended daily dosage of Chinese SWING:

* *Begin with 150 repetitions of the exercise. After the second week, add 20 each day until you can do 1,000 repetitions, which takes about 30 minutes.*

* *After swinging 200-300 times you may experience gas, hiccups, sweat, flush and even feel sore in the legs. These are signs that the digestion is starting to function better and the energy is circulating throughout the body organs.*

* *Don't tire yourself by overdoing it! For maximum benefit, do the SWING outside in the fresh air.*

Submitted by Mary O'Brien Sippel.

101 CLOUDS TO SUNSHINE

This adaptation of a traditional T'ai Chi exercise allows participants to breathe and stretch easily while imagining four different scenes from nature.

GOALS

1) To focus attention and let go of mental distractions.

2) To stretch and release tension from the muscles in the arms and back.

GROUP SIZE

Unlimited, as long as there is space to stretch comfortably.

TIME FRAME

3-5 minutes; may be repeated several times.

PROCESS

Note: Be sure to practice this sequence ahead of time so you can describe and demonstrate it easily.

1) The trainer invites participants to stand and join in a revitalizing stretch based upon traditional T'ai Chi movements.

2) The trainer demonstrates as she reads the instructions for the CLOUDS - RAIN - RAINBOW - SUNSHINE exercise sequence.

Note: You may want to add to the scene by suggesting that participants imagine that there is a pool or pond of water evaporating on a warm day. The energy flows up as the moisture rises and the participants lift their arms toward the sky.

3) Participants repeat the sequence one or more times.

Submitted by Marti Belknap.

CLOUDS - RAIN - RAINBOW - SUNSHINE

CLOUDS   Stand with your knees relaxed and your hands cupped
                in front of your pelvis.

                Inhale and draw energy up from the earth through
                your body.

                Invert your hands and "push the clouds" toward the
                sky.

RAIN   Exhale and lower your arms in an arc down to your
                sides.

                Allow the "rain to fall" gently upon the earth.

RAINBOW   Clasp your hands together behind your back and lift
                your arms as you inhale.

                Exhale and bend forward with your arms extended
                behind you.

                "Form a rainbow" with your body over the land.

                Inhale and lift, relax arms to sides and exhale.

SUNSHINE   Turn your palms upward and lift your arms in an arc
                overhead as you inhale.

                Exhale and embrace the sunshine with your arms
                making a circle in front of your chest.

                Inhale and "draw the sunshine" into your heart.

                Exhale and feel the sun bathe your body.

102 DO-IT-YOURSELF SINGALONG

Participants compose stress and coping lyrics for familiar melodies and then perform their "work" for the group.

GOALS

1) To reinforce concepts taught in the session or course.

2) To promote group creativity and spontaneity.

GROUP SIZE

Unlimited

TIME FRAME

10-15 minutes; longer with larger groups.

MATERIALS NEEDED

Newsprint or overhead transparencies

PROCESS

1) The trainer announces that during the next 10 minutes everyone will have an opportunity to demonstrate their creative abilities by helping to compose a song that incorporates something they have learned about stress or coping during this course (session/workshop).

2) The trainer divides participants into small groups of 3-6 persons and assigns each group a different tune to use as the melody (eg, Three Blind Mice; Row, Row, Row Your Boat; Silent Night; America; Frere Jacques; Twinkle, Twinkle Little Star; school fight songs, etc).

    Note: You may want to give an example like the following to prime the pump and get the humor flowing --

    > *(to the tune of Three Blind Mice)*
    > *Much less stress! Much less stress!*
    > *We've all learned how to cope with it,*
    > *Not eat or drink or smoke with it!*
    > *Just breathe and stretch and joke with it!*
    > *Much less stress! Much less stress!*

3) The trainer provides each group with newsprint or over-head transparencies and markers to use in recording their final lyrics for all to see.

4) After about 10 minutes the trainer notifies groups that
     there are only a few minutes left and encourages them
     to get their songs recorded.

     *Note: You may need to remind people that the songs
           don't have to be perfect -- just fun!*

5) As soon as the groups are ready the trainer asks each in
     turn to come up front and teach their song to the
     others.   They many want to demonstrate first and then
     invite all participants to join in the singing.

     After all have "performed", the large group may want to
     choose one of the creations as their special theme song
     to be repeated periodically throughout the rest of the
     learning experience.

TRAINER'S NOTES

103 GROANS AND MOANS

In this noisy energizer participants experiment with groaning, an old-fashioned remedy for stress.

GOALS

1) To demonstrate the effectiveness of groaning as a tension-relieving technique.

2) To relax and let go.

GROUP SIZE

Unlimited; it may be difficult to persuade a very small group or an especially formal one to try this technique.

TIME FRAME

15 minutes

MATERIALS NEEDED

Tape recorder, recording of soulful instrumental jazz such as Coltrane, Brubek, Miles Davis, etc.

PHYSICAL SETTING

Works especially well when the room is carpeted and participants can spread out on the floor, but the exercise can also be done seated in chairs.

PROCESS

1) The trainer invites participants to experiment with a natural, easy, healthy, old-fashioned technique for dealing with unavoidable pain, emotional pressures and stress -- groaning. As participants groan in disbelief at her announcement, she continues by outlining several benefits of the therapeutic groan:

- Groaning helps you relax physically by stimulating deep, regulated breathing, maximizing oxygen intake and exercising the diaphragm.

- As you relax, the vibrations of the groan in your throat, chest and sinuses provide a tension-shedding internal massage.

- The process of groaning creates a focus for concentration that can still the restless mind.

2) The trainer invites participants to stretch out
    comfortably on the floor or in their chairs. Once
    everyone is settled, she demonstrates several deep,
    full-bodied groans and announces that the group will
    practice groaning for 5 or 10 minutes.

    *Note: To avoid straining the voice, the flow of air from
    the windpipe should not be restricted. Ask parti-
    cipants to experiment, moving their heads until
    they find the position where their groan is most
    open-flowing and effortless, even when the sound
    is quite loud.*

    The trainer reassures the group that it's perfectly
    normal to feel a little silly and embarrassed, at least
    at first -- and it's ok to giggle! She suggests that
    participants close their eyes while she plays some music
    that should help cover the uproar.

3) The trainer asks people to start groaning -- and then
    encourages, prods, cajoles, challenges, cheers the group
    as necessary to get them going and to help them through
    the first moments of giggling and confusion.

    *Note: Be sure to keep groaning with the group so they
    don't run out of steam. With a potentially
    resistant group it helps to have a conspirator
    planted in the audience to help.*

4) After 7-10 minutes of deep groaning (the more, the
    better) the trainer invites people to slowly and gently
    return their awareness to the room and describe their
    experiences. As people share, the trainer uses the data
    generated to highlight the potential benefits and appli-
    cations of groaning:

    ● A groan can be used as a pressure valve to deal with
      a stress overload by releasing a strong overflow of
      pressure or pain while it's still building up.

    ● Any time you need temporary relief of tension,
      exhaustion or other emotional pain, you can simply
      groan!

    ● The incongruity of humor and laughter that sometimes
      arises in the midst of groaning can provide enjoy-
      able -- and perhaps healing -- relief!

Submitted by Louis M Savary.

104 TUG OF WAR

In this game of strategy, participants pair up to explore alternative approaches to conflict.

GOALS

1) To assist individuals in obtaining a glimpse of their personal style at approaching conflict.

GROUP SIZE

Minimum of 8-10 people

TIME FRAME

5-10 minutes

PROCESS

1) The trainer defines conflict and announces that during the next 5 minutes participants will join in an experiment to discover/rediscover how they typically approach conflict situations. She then asks everyone to stand up and find a partner.

2) Once everyone has a partner, the trainer gives each pair a piece of paper, asking them to decide which one should hold it.

   Note: "Playfair" techniques could be substituted here. Instead of asking partners to decide who should hold the paper, ask them to decide who is the zucchini and who is the artichoke (or who is the penguin and who the flamingo, etc). You can then announce that the zucchinis (or penguins) will hold the paper first.

3) The person holding the paper is instructed to hold on to it and not let go under any circumstances. The partner not holding the paper is asked to get the paper from the other person, any way they can. The trainer announces there will be exactly one minute to accomplish this task.

   Note: During the exercise the trainer will want to observe closely and note interactions that illustrate different styles of resolving conflict (eg, some people will grab, others will wheedle or sweet talk and some may even offer cash).

4) After one minute the trainer calls time and asks participants to switch roles and repeat the exercise.

5) At the end of one minute, time is called and the
trainer invites participants to describe what they
noticed about their style of approaching a conflict
situation.

TRAINER'S NOTES

Submitted by Jan Berry-Schroeder.

105 WARM HANDS

In this brief introduction to the potential of autogenics, participants imagine their way to warm hands and a profound sense of relaxation.

GOALS

1) To demonstrate the power of autogenic-like techniques for relaxation.

TIME FRAME

5-10 minutes

PROCESS

1) The trainer invites participants to experiment with an effective relaxation technique that is based on visualization and autogenics -- a process of self-regulation that uses mental imagery and the power of suggestion to counteract the physical side effects of stress.

   Note: You might warn participants that if anyone feels anxious or uncomfortable during the experience, they should stop the imagery process at once and take a break.

2) Participants are directed to assume a tension-free position -- seated with arms supported on the thighs, hands between the knees, shoulders slightly shrugged, body balanced over the pelvis and eyes closed.

   The trainer encourages participants to adopt an attitude of passive concentration, focusing on the words and images as they are suggested, then repeating the phrase silently several times in the silence between.

   The trainer slowly reads the WARM HANDS instructions, pausing long enough at each image so that people can mentally review the phrase two or three times before moving on.

   Note: Keep your voice steady and the pace even as you read. Try not to emphasize any words. It should sound monotonous!

Submitted by David Danskin.

WARM HANDS

Let's begin by taking a deep breath. Inhale, filling
your lungs with air all the way down to the belly. Now
exhale slowly with a soft "whooshing" sound.

Take another deep breath . . . and imagine as you
breathe out that all the tension is leaving your body. .

Imagine your hands as warm -- relaxed and warm . . .
Say to yourself slowly four times . . .
MY HANDS ARE WARM, RELAXED AND WARM . . .
(pause 15 seconds)

Now visualize your hands in a bucket of warm water . . .
or near a roaring fire . . .
Stay with that image as you slowly say to yourself . . .
MY HANDS ARE WARM, RELAXED AND WARM . . .
(pause 15 seconds)

Make your mental image as vivid as possible as you
warm your hands in this comfortable cozy way . . .
Reminding yourself again . . .
MY HANDS ARE WARM, RELAXED AND WARM . . .
(pause)

As you continue to visualize your hands becoming warmer
and more relaxed . . . perhaps you can even begin to
allow the blood to flow down your arms . . . and into
your hands . . . leaving them feeling warmer and warmer
. . . and more and more relaxed . . .
Let that feeling of warmth and relaxation spread down
your arms and into your hands as you say to yourself . .
MY HANDS ARE WARM . . . RELAXED AND WARM . . .
(pause)

Now allow that pleasant feeling of warmth to spread
throughout your body as you tell yourself . . .
I AM CALM AND RELAXED . . .
(pause)

Continue to enjoy this feeling of warmth and relaxation
as you prepare to turn your attention from the inner you
to the outer world . . .
Before you open your eyes . . mentally prepare for your
return by saying several times to your self . . .
WHEN I OPEN MY EYES I WILL FEEL RELAXED, FRESH AND ALERT
(pause)

When you are ready . . . please open your eyes . . .

106 WHAT'S THE HURRY?

This touching parable points out how striving too hard to reach a goal may have stressful side effects.

GOALS

1) To help participants reflect on the potential risks of Type A behavior.

GROUP SIZE

Unlimited

TIME FRAME

5-10 minutes

PROCESS

Note: This story will have maximum impact if it is included to illustrate or top off a presentation on Type A behavior.

1) The trainer reads the parable, "What's the Hurry?"

WHAT'S THE HURRY?

There once was a fellow who, with his father, farmed a little piece of land.
Several times a year they'd load up the ox-cart with vegetables and drive to the nearest city.

Except for their names and the patch of ground, father and son had little in common.
The old man believed in taking it easy . . . and the son was the go-getter type.

One morning, they loaded the cart, hitched up the ox and set out.
The young fellow figured that if they kept going all day and night, they'd get to the market by next morning.
He walked alongside the ox and kept prodding it with a stick.

"Take it easy," said the old man. "You'll last longer."

"If we get to market ahead of the others," said his
son, "we have a better chance of getting good prices."

The old man pulled his hat down over his eyes and
went to sleep on the seat.
Four miles and four hours down the road, they came
to a little house.
"Here's your uncle's place," said the father, waking
up. "Let's stop in and say hello."
"We've lost an hour already," complained the go-
getter.

"Then a few minutes more won't matter," said his
father. "My brother and I live so close, yet we see
each other so seldom."

The young man fidgeted while the two old gentlemen
gossiped away an hour.
On the move again, the father tooks his turn leading
the ox.
By and by, they came to a fork in the road.
The old man directed the ox to the right.
"The left is the shorter way," said the boy.

"I know it," said the old man, "but this way is
prettier."

"Have you no respect for time?" asked the impatient
young man.

"I respect it very much," said the old fellow.
That's why I like to use it for looking at pretty
things."

The right-hand path led through woodland and wild
flowers.
The young man was so busy watching the sun sink he
didn't notice how lovely the sunset was.
Twilight found them in what looked like one big
garden.
"Let's sleep here," said the old man.

"This is the last trip I take with you," snapped his
son. "You're more interested in flowers than in
making money."

"That's the nicest thing you've said in a long
time," smiled the old fellow.
A minute later he was asleep.
A little before sunrise, the young man shook his
father awake. They hitched up and went on.
A mile and an hour away they came upon a farmer
trying to pull his cart out of a ditch.

© 1986 Whole Person Press PO Box 3151 Duluth MN 55803

"Let's give him a hand," said the father.

"And lose more time?" exploded the son.
"Relax," said the old man. "You might be in a ditch sometime yourself."

By the time the other cart was back on the road, it was almost eight o'clock.
Suddenly a great flash of lightening split the sky.
Then there was thunder.
Beyond the hills, the heavens grew dark.

"Looks like a big rain in the city," said the old man.

"If we had been on time, we'd be sold out by now," grumbled his son.

"Take it easy," said the old gentleman, "you'll last longer."

It wasn't until late in the afternoon that they got to the top of the hill overlooking the town.
They looked down at it for a long time.
Neither of them spoke.

Finally the young man who had been in such a hurry said, "I see what you mean, father."

They turned their cart around and drove away from what had once been the city of Hiroshima.

2) When the reading is finished and before the mood of the group is broken, the trainer may ask participants to write down a sentence or two describing the meaning and message of this parable in their current life situation.

3) After a few minutes for reflection, the trainer may ask for insights, observations and examples.

This story is attributed to Billy Rose who included it in one of his "Pitching Horseshoes" columns.

© 1986 Whole Person Press PO Box 3151 Duluth MN 55803

107 YOU'RE NOT LISTENING!

In this riotous energizer partners work hard at "not listening" to each other and the group brainstorms essential components of good listening.

GOALS

1) To identify key elements of effective listening.

2) To promote group interaction and playfulness.

TIME FRAME

5-10 minutes

PROCESS

Note: This process is an ideal icebreaker for a presentation on listening as a stress management skill. It would fit well with STOP LOOK AND LISTEN, p 84.

1) The trainer asks everyone to stand up, mill around the room and grab a partner. In each dyad, partners decide who is HONOLULU and who is FORT LAUDERDALE.

2) The trainer announces that this is an exercise in not listening. Partners will take turns. FORT LAUDERDALES will begin by speaking spontaneously on an assigned topic for 30 seconds. While they are speaking, the HONOLULUS should somehow communicate that they are not listening to their partner.

Note: Encourage the "speakers" to put a little punch into their presentation -- to speak with energy, passion and pizzazz! Encourage "listeners" to be creative in their non-response.

3) Once the rules are clear, the trainer instructs FORT LAUDERDALES to vividly describe their favorite ice cream to the HONOLULU partner, who will not listen. (30-45 seconds)

4) The trainer calls time and asks partners to switch roles. This time the HONOLULUS describe in detail their favorite vacation -- real or ideal -- while the FORT LAUDERDALES demonstrate not listening. (30-45 seconds)

5) Since this "not listening" exercise frustrates direct communication, the trainer offers an opportunity for more satisfying contact. He announces that partners now

have 10 seconds to make a positive connection with each
other in some creative way.

6) After the buzz settles down, participants are instructed
to join another pair, and in quartets, spend 2 minutes
brainstorming responses to the question:

   ❑ Based on your recent experience of not being
   listened to, what are the key components of
   effective listening?

7) The trainer reconvenes the group, solicits examples of
good listening components and ties this process into
other issues raised in the learning experience.

VARIATIONS

■ In Step 6, groups make newsprint posters of DO'S AND DONT'S
FOR LISTENING. These are posted around the room and used as
reminders of listening guidelines in later small group
discussions.

■ Repeat Steps 3 & 4, only this time the listeners try to
communicate that they are listening intently and with
understanding. Use new topics such as "favorite movie" or
"favorite TV show" or "favorite restaurant" or "favorite
place in your town", etc.

■ In Step 5, groups brainstorm lists of non-verbal cues that
indicate "listening" and those that indicate "not
listening". They then discuss the impact of non-verbals on
the communication process and the relationship to stress.

TRAINER'S NOTES

Submitted by Joel Goodman.

108 PUSHING MY BUTTONS

In this unusual self-care break participants stimulate several accupressure points to get their energy flowing again.

GOALS

1) To introduce the concept of energy flow.

2) To energize and revitalize the group.

TIME FRAME

10-15 minutes

PROCESS

1) The trainer invites participants to join her in a healthy wake-up break based on self-accupressure techniques interpreted from ancient writings found on the walls of the Shaolin Temple in China.

She explains that participants will be massaging specific areas of their own bodies, including many "pressure points", where the body's energy flow can be stimulated. Each person will discover the exact location of his own pressure points by noticing the spots that feel "different" or a little tender. Steady pressure or gentle massage should relieve the pain and release the energy.

2) The trainer suggests that everyone follow along as she talks the group through the 13 steps, describing and demonstrating the various strokes that are used for the different points.

Note: Be sure to experiment with these instructions and find your own pressure points before trying to explain them to the group.

VARIATION

■ A few of these accupressure points could be introduced at each break. Then, toward the end of the learning experience, the whole sequence could be done as a unit.

Submitted by Jackie Mosier who learned a process similar to this from her T'ai Chi instructor, Master Marshall Ho.

PUSHING MY BUTTONS
self-accupressure routine

1) Rub the top of your head briskly with both palms.

2) Use both thumbs to locate the depression at the base of
    your skull in back, where it meets the spine. Starting in
    the middle and moving out toward the sides, staying just
    below the bony (occipital) ridge, locate pressure points
    about one inch apart all across the base of the skull.

    Most people have several tender spots in this area, so
    don't hurry -- use enough pressure with your thumbs to
    "feel" the tenderness at each spot, but not enough pressure
    to create acute pain. After a few seconds this press can
    be released or expanded into a gentle circular massage.
    Then move on to the next spot.

3) Rub your nose vigorously, kneading, pulling and moving it
    around. Try a two-handed noserub!

4) Massage the lobe of each ear between your thumb and index
    finger. Make sure the whole perimeter gets a thorough
    rubdown, then pull gently. Finally, cup your hands over
    your ears and give the whole area a quick up and down rub.

5) Use your thumbs to trace along and beneath your lower jaw.
    Use moderate pressure and move very slowly. Start in the
    corners under the ears and follow the jaw bone to the
    midline, thumbs meeting under your chin.

6) Using the fingers of your right hand, rub across your chest
    from the left shoulder to the sternum, staying below the
    line of the collarbone. Hold your fingers like a curved
    garden rake and make strong back-and-forth movements,
    kneading the muscles as you slowly move across your chest.
    Repeat on the left side using the right hand.

7) Flex your left arm. Use your right thumb to locate the
    pressure point in the crook of your elbow, just outside the
    bone of your lower arm. Feel around, using a fair amount
    of pressure until you find the trigger point. Hold and
    release. Repeat for the right elbow.

8) Use the thumb and one finger of your right hand to circle
    your left wrist. Hold your hand steady and quickly rotate
    your left arm in a screwing motion so that the left wrist
    gets a vigorous massage. Repeat for the right wrist.

9) Make fists with both hands. Now reach back and gently pound
    the kidney area with your fists. At this angle you should
    get just enough pressure for stimulation.

10) Using both hands in a rhythmic motion, clap and slap both
     thighs up and down and front and back, as far as you can
     reach and as long as it feels good!

11) Move down to the area of your kneecap. Using short back-
     and-forth strokes with your fingertips, knead the entire
     area above, around and below the kneecap, extending down to
     massage the protrusions below and outside of the kneecap.
     If you find any tender spots, stop, apply more pressure and
     release.

12) Run your thumb along the inside of your shin to a point
     about 4 fingers above the ankle bone. When you find the
     tender spot, use a thumb press for several seconds, release
     and then repeat. Be sure to stimulate the pressure point
     on both legs.

     Note: Pregnant women should not stimulate this point.

13) Use whatever strokes feel good and as much time as possible
     massaging your feet. Try thumb circles, kneading, pulling,
     clapping, rubbing -- on the top, bottom, sides, edges,
     between the toes, along the arch, etc. If the room is
     carpeted, try rubbing the soles of your feet vigorously on
     the floor.

CONTRIBUTORS

MARTHA BELKNAP, MA. Salina Star Route, Gold Hill, Boulder CO
80302. 303/447-YOGA. Marti is an educational consultant
with a specialty in creative relaxation and stress management skills. She has 25 years of teaching experience at all
levels. Marti offers relaxation workshops and creativity
courses in schools, universities, hospitals and business.

JAN BERRY-SCHROEDER, MEd. Director, Employee Assistance Program,
Evanston Hospital, 2650 Ridge Ave, Evanston IL 60201.
313/492-2000. Jan is a consultant, therapist and writer.
She has extensive experience in Employee Assistance Programs
and integrating wellness into the work place. She specializes in stress management, conflict resolution, woman's
issues and self-esteem -- to all of which she adds fun.

JIM CATHCART, CPAE. PO Box 9075, La Jolla CA 92038. 619/459-
1515. Jim is the author of numerous books, audio and video
programs in the category of WINNING WITH PEOPLE, tm. He is
best known for the development of the concept RELATIONSHIP
STRATEGIES, published by Nightengale-Conant Corporation.

DAVID G DANSKIN, PhD. Counseling Psychologist. Counseling
Center, Kansas State University, Manhattan KS 66506.
913/532-6927 (work) 913/539-4676 (home). David is author of
QUICKI-MINI STRESS-MANAGEMENT STRATEGIES FOR WORK, HOME,
LEISURE and is developing special versions for persons with
disabilities. He is also senior author of BIOFEEDBACK: AN
INTRODUCTION AND GUIDE. David offers workshops on quicki-
mini strategies and deep relaxation training for educators,
other professionals, laypersons and students.

ROBERT C FELLOWS, MTS (Harvard University). MindMatters Workshops, PO Box 691566, Los Angeles CA 90069. 213/934-9960.
Bob is an internationally known magician who specializes in
ESP. This intriguing talent not only helps him to get
people's attention -- it also provides graphic illustrations
for psychological points. A regular presenter at the
National Wellness Conference and at colleges throughout the
US, Bob recently toured Australia, promoting wellness for
their Department of Sport and Recreation.

JOSEPH J GIACALONE, MPH. Counseling & Career Ctr, Regis College,
W 50th Ave & Lowell Blvd, Denver CO 80210. 303/458-3507
(work) 303/759-8302 (home). Joe is a health educator and
career counselor. In addition to his work with students and
mid-career adults at Regis, Joe maintains a private practice
working with individuals, businesses and health care provid-
ers in developing survival strategies for dealing with the
health implications of lifestyle and organizational change.

JERRY GLASHAGEL. Consultant. 32 Drexel, LaGrange IL 60525.
312/352-3995. Jerry has spent 20 years with the YMCA in
India, New York, Pasadena, Akron and Chicago. From 1980 to
1986 he has been responsible for YMCA program development
nationally. Jerry has degrees from the University of
Illinois and Yale University, and enjoys facilitating
groups, product design, writing and training.

JOEL GOODMAN, EdD. Director, The Humor Project, 110 Spring St,
Saratoga Springs NY 12866. 518/587-8770. Dr Joel Goodman
is a popular speaking consultant and wellness seminar
leader who has worked with over 70,000 corporate managers,
health care professionals, educators, and other helping
professionals in focusing on the positive power of humor.
Author of 7 books, he also edits LAUGHING MATTERS magazine,
which has received rave reviews throughout the US and
abroad.

PAT MILLER. 1211 N Basswood Ave, Duluth MN 55811. 218/722-9361.
Pat operates her own training and consulting business called
"Meeting with Success." In addition to her specialty --
conflict management training -- Pat also offers workshops in
running better meetings, leadership training, public speaking, self-enrichment through building self-confidence and
assertiveness.

JACKI MOSIER, RN. Certified Family Nurse Practitioner. Accu-
pressurist. PO Box 845, Flagstaff AZ 86002. 602/774-1089.
As a health care professional, Jacki has found a combination
of traditional western medical practices, ancient practices
involving energy flows and spiritual recognition necessary
to achieve good health and wellness.

LOUIS M SAVARY, PhD. 5201 MacArthur Terrace NW, Washington DC
20016. 202/364-1075. Holder of doctorates in mathematics
and spirituality, Louis is co-founder of the Institute for
Consciousness and Music and author of several books including SOUND HEALTH (with Steven Halpern) and PASSAGES: A
GUIDE FOR PILGRIMS OF THE MIND.

MARCIA A SCHNORR, RN MS. Nursing Instructor, Kishwaukee College,
Rt 38 & Malta Rd, Malta IL 60150. 815/825-2086 (work)
815/562-6823 (home). Marcia has a MS in nursing with empha-
sis in both medical-surgical nursing and community mental
health nursing. She is currently a doctoral student in
adult continuing education with a major interest in adding
the spiritual dimension to nursing service and education.
Marcia demonstrates her interest in the whole person through
her roles as nursing instructor, social ministry ombudsman,
and independent consultant.

KEITH W SEHNERT, MD.   4210 Fremont Ave S, Minneapolis MN 55409.
    612/721-2951 (work) 612/824-5134 (home). Keith is a family
    doctor who has become a leader in the medical self-care
    movement. He spends much energy in print (HOW TO BE YOUR
    OWN DOCTOR - SOMETIMES, STRESS/UNSTRESS and SELF-
    CARE/WELLNESS) and in person urging people to improve their
    physical, mental and spiritual well-being. He has a clini-
    cal affiliation with Trinity Health Care Clinic in
    Minneapolis.

MARY O'BRIEN SIPPEL, RN MS.   517 Lincoln Park Dr, Duluth MN
    55806. 218/723-6130 (work) 218/722-8136 (home). Mary is
    still one of Whole Person Associates' most enthusiastic
    faculty. Now a counselor and faculty member at the College
    of St Scholastica, Mary continues to inspire others to care
    for themselves and stay vital. Mary's experience in teach-
    ing stress management across the country has enabled her to
    be her own best caretaker as career woman, wife and mother
    of two toddlers.

SALLY STROSAHL, MA. Marriage & Family Therapist. 436 Watson,
    Aurora IL 60505. 312/851-4446. Sally has an MA in clinical
    psychology; trained at the Wholistic Health Center;
    researched the relationship between stress and illness. In
    addition to her private practice in marriage and family
    therapy, Sally frequently presents workshops in the areas of
    stress management, burnout, support groups, parenting and
    combining career and motherhood. She particularly enjoys
    working with "systems" (family, work groups, agencies,
    business, churches) to help enhance each member's growth and
    well-being.

MARK WARNER, EdS.   Office of Residence Life, James Madison
    University, Harrisonburg VA 22807. 703/568-6275. Mark is
    a residence life professional who coordinates human develop-
    ment programming and staff training. In addition to his
    residence life duties he consults, writes, and presents on
    the topic of Wellness Promotion and Program Development.
    His main emphasis is wellness promotion in higher education.

RANDY R WEIGEL, PhD. Human Development Specialist, Iowa State
    University, Ames IA 50011. 515/294-8754. Through work-
    shops, study guides and media development, Randy specializes
    in making stress research understandable and usable by lay
    audiences. His training in human relations and education
    allows him to tailor programs to the needs of specific
    audiences. Randy has trained students, faculty, parents,
    farmers and helping professionals in stress management.

THE EDITORS

All Handbook exercises not specifically documented are the creative efforts of the editors who have been designing, collecting and experimenting with structured processes in their teaching, training and consultation work since the late 1960's.

Nancy Loving Tubesing, EdD, holds a masters degree in group counseling and a doctorate in counselor education. She served as editor of the Society for Wholistic Medicine's monograph series and articulated the principles of whole person health care in the monograph, **Philosophical Assumptions**. A Faculty Associate and Publications Director at Whole Person Associates, Nancy is currently channeling her creative energies into the development of the Handbook series and the compilation and testing of exercises for future volumes.

Donald A Tubesing, MDiv, PhD, designer of the widely acclaimed STRESS SKILLS seminar and author of **Kicking Your Stress Habits**, has been a pioneer in the movement to reintegrate the body, mind and spirit in health care delivery. With his background in psychology, theology and education, Don brings the whole person perspective to his consultation in business and industry, government agencies and hundreds of health care and human service systems.

Nancy and Don have collaborated on many writing projects over the years, beginning with a small group college orientation project in 1970 and including a self-help book on whole person wellness, **The Caring Question** (Minneapolis: Augsburg, 1983) and a new 8-session stress course for the National YMCA, **The Y's Way to Stress Management**.

© 1986 Whole Person Press PO Box 3151 Duluth MN 55803

FUTURE CONTRIBUTORS

If you develop an exciting, effective structured exercise you'd like to share with other trainers in the field of stress management or wellness promotion, please send it to us for consideration using the following guidelines:

1) Your entry should be written in a format similar to those in this Handbook.

2) Contributors must either guarantee that the materials they submit are not previously copyrighted or provide a copyright release for inclusion in the Whole Person Handbook series.

3) When you have adapted from the work of others, please acknowledge the original source of ideas or activities.

4) Include a brief (40 words) creative biography similar to those above.

All contributors will be acknowledged on receipt. The editors will review each submission and test it with one or more groups before reaching a decision about inclusion.

WHOLE PERSON PUBLICATIONS

KICKING YOUR STRESS HABITS:
A do-it-yourself guide for coping with stress

by Donald A Tubesing, MDiv, PhD

Striking graphics highlight this unusual "workshop-in-a-book" which actively engages readers in identifying sources of stress and resources for coping. Full of examples, worksheets, checklists, practical ideas and a planning process that really works! Ideal for classroom or group setting. Large format paperback, $10.00.

THE CARING QUESTION
You first or me first — choosing a healthy balance

by Donald A Tubesing & Nancy Loving Tubesing

Thought-provoking questions are scattered throughout this startling challenge to the wellness revolution. Filled with wit and wisdom, **The Caring Question** invites readers to move beyond wellness to a life that balances self-care with caring for others. Paperback, $3.95.

WHOLE PERSON HEALTH CARE: Philosophical Assumptions

by Nancy Loving Tubesing

This slim volume is packed with insights concerning the nature and form of whole person health care along with snapshots of the theory in practice, challenges to practitioners, and suggestions for research. Paperback, $6.00.

IN OUR OWN HANDS
A woman's book of self-help therapy

by Sheila Ernst and Lucy Goodison

This practical guidebook for starting a self-help group belongs in the library of every professional who works with groups. Clear, concise descriptions of several theoretical approaches are interspersed with oodles of outstanding exercises that any group could try. Add 143 techniques to your bag of tricks. Paperback, $9.95.

© 1986 Whole Person Press   PO Box 3151   Duluth MN 55803

TAPE/WORKBOOK TRAINING PACKAGES

STRESS SKILLS: Strategies for Managing Stress

Voice-over narration guides the listener through the celebrated STRESS SKILLS seminar experience captured in these recordings. Concept essays precede each worksheet in the Participant Workbook and highlight topics such as: the nature of stress, taking control of stress, choice and change, whole person stress analysis and 20 stress skills. Perfect for individual or small group study, this resource would be a valuable addition to any staff training library. Six cassettes with companion workbook, $95.00. Workbook only, $7.50.

TUNE IN: Listening Skills Workshop

TUNE IN is a carefully developed and extensively tested empathy training workshop you can conduct yourself. The 16 hours of tape-led group experiences help participants develop competency in basic listening and empathy skills. Currently used around the world for inservice training of counselors, teachers, physicians, hospital personnel, volunteers, nurses, clergy, office staff, managers and administrators. Workshop tapes, Leader Manual and Participant Workbook, $95.00. Workbook only, $7.50.

PERSONAL RECHARGING: Rx for Burnout in the Workplace

Carefully edited, attractively packaged cassette recordings of a live PERSONAL RECHARGING workshop can be used with the accompanying Participant Workbook to create the seminar atmosphere and process. Topics include: symptoms, stages and causes; stress/vitality in the workplace; individual revitalization strategies; interpersonal support networking and planning for renewal. Order this package for conducting your own workshop or to share with friends and colleagues. Tape and workbook, $95.00. Workbook only, $7.50

UNUSUAL CASSETTE TAPES

RELAX . . . LET GO . . . RELAX

Music by Steven Halpern provides the calming background for a 30 minute "end of the day" relaxation sequence for shedding tension, and a 20 minute "anytime of the day" revitalization routine. Male and female narration, $9.00.

SPIRITUAL CENTERING: An inward journey of renewal

In this non-judgmental exploration of personal spiritual depths, Don Tubesing guides listeners through a process of quieting and centering that allows each person to discover her own internal wisdom. Useful as a discussion starter or closing motivator. Flip side with Halpern Sounds musical background, $9.00.

FINGERTIP FACE MASSAGE: A gentle self care break

In her warm and gentle manner, Mary O'Brien Sippel guides listeners through a refreshing self-massage process. The 10-minute experience generates a feeling of relaxation, well-being and renewed vitality. Use this tape as an "energy break" during long sessions or to kick off your presentation of self-care options. Flip side with Halpern Sounds musical background, $9.00.

DAYDREAMS: A week's worth of get-aways

You deserve a mini-vacation from stress and strain. Now you can use the movie screen in your mind to unstress yourself, and take a relaxing guided journey . . . to a sunswept mountain top . . . in the mesmerizing night sky . . . to a cozy cabin retreat . . . for an invigorating sail . . . to a bubbling hot spring . . . Five different 10-minute get-aways with Halpern Sounds musical background, $9.00

BEYOND PEPTALKS AND HANDOUTS

Effective teaching helps people move beyond information to implementation. In this practical presentation, process education expert Dr Don Tubesing shares his philosophy and time-tested techniques for getting participants involved in the learning experience, $9.00.

YOU ALONE CAN BE WELL . . . But you can't be well alone!

In this keynote speech from Wellness Promo VII, Dr Donald Tubesing addresses the issue of wellness from the whole person perspective, asking the question, "What's the point of being well?" Listeners are asked to reflect on the self/other care balance in their lives. A humorous, challenging, positive 90 minutes, $9.00.

THE WHOLE PERSON HANDBOOKS
for trainers, educators and group leaders

STRUCTURED EXERCISES IN STRESS MANAGEMENT

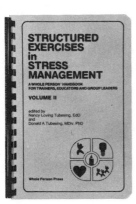

Nancy Loving Tubesing, EdD and
Donald A Tubesing, PhD, Editors

Volume 1 (orange cover) contains 36 ready-to-use teaching designs that involve the participant as a whole person in learning to manage stress more effectively. These exercises help motivate people to identify desired changes, build new coping skills and plan for a healthier lifestyle.

This practical resource includes icebreakers, stress assessments, management strategies, skill builders, action planners and group energizers. Spiral bound, flexible plastic cover, $19.95.

Volume 2 (red cover) and **Volume 3** (yellow cover) each contain 36 all new process teaching ideas in the same easy-to-use format, $19.95 each.

STRUCTURED EXERCISES IN WELLNESS PROMOTION

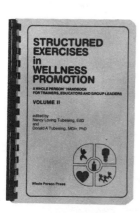

Nancy Loving Tubesing, EdD and
Donald A Tubesing, PhD, Editors

Volume 1 (green cover) includes 36 experiential learning activities that focus on whole person health — body, mind, spirit, emotions, relationships. These exercises encourage people to adopt a wellness-oriented attitude and develop more responsible self-care patterns.

This handy volume contains icebreakers, wellness explorations, self-care strategies, action planners and group energizers. Spiral bound, soft plastic cover, $19.95.

Volume 2 (blue cover) and **Volume 3** (purple cover) each include 36 totally different individual and group exercises that promote wellness, $19.95 each.

© 1986 Whole Person Press PO Box 3151 Duluth MN 55803

THE STRESS KIT

Whole Person Press is proud to announce the latest innovation in stress management resources — a multimedia kit that stresses creative coping. Designed by Whole Person Associates as a health promotion tool for a major insurance company, **The Stress Kit** is now available for your personal or professional use.

The kit includes three educational components — PILEUP (a card game), The Stress Examiner (an unusual newspaper) and Stress Talk/StressRelease (cassette tape programs). This $45.80 value is available packaged together in an attractive bookshelf container for only $29.95. The components may also be purchased separately.

Use one or more of these fun-filled pieces with staff, clients, students, team members, family or friends. You'll understand stress better — and discover positive, effective coping strategies.

PILEUP

A deck of 108 colorful stress and coping cards with instructions for 12 self-discovery games. Card sorts, role plays, assessments, simulations and games graphically demonstrate how stress piles up and how creativity can expand your coping capabilities. Super for families or work teams! $15.95 separately.

The Stress Examiner

This 12-page, 4-color newspaper (USA Today format) is bursting with information and activities for readers of all ages. Test your stress quotient. Play Penny Pileup. Read how celebrities cope. Find out about stress and how to deal with it in every day situations. A book-full of ideas — yet so much more readable! $3.95 separately.

Stress Talk/StressRelease

Side A (Stress Talk) of this tape provides a mini-workshop that guides an individual or group in exploring personal stress patterns and management styles. Reproducible worksheets are included for group use. $15.95 separately.

Side B (StressRelease) features a special "radio broadcast" that teaches simple, effective techniques to relieve tension. The program ends with a 15-minute progressive relaxation exercise, complete with mood music. $9.95 separately.

© 1986 Whole Person Press PO Box 3151 Duluth MN 55803

ORDER FORM

Name _____

Address _____

_____

City _____

State _____ Zip _____

Please make checks payable
and send to:
Whole Person Associates Inc
PO Box 3151
Duluth MN 55803
218/728-6807

WHOLE PERSON HANDBOOKS for trainers, educators & group leaders

Structured Exercises in Stress Management
☐ Volume 1 (orange cover, 1983) . . . .   19.95   _____
☐ Volume 2 (red cover, 1984) . . . .   19.95   _____
☐ Volume 3 (yellow cover, 1986) . . . .   19.95   _____

Structured Exercises in Wellness Promotion
☐ Volume 1 (green cover, 1983) . . . .   19.95   _____
☐ Volume 2 (blue cover, 1984) . . . .   19.95   _____
☐ Volume 3 (purple cover, 1986) . . . .   19.95   _____

TAPE/WORKBOOK TRAINING PACKAGES
☐ STRESS SKILLS workshop . . . .   95.00   _____
☐ TUNE IN workshop . . . .   95.00   _____
☐ PERSONAL RECHARGING workshop . . . .   95.00   _____

WORKBOOKS ONLY
☐ STRESS SKILLS Participant Workbook . . . .   7.50   _____
☐ TUNE IN Participant Workbook . . . .   7.50   _____
☐ PERSONAL RECHARGING Participant Workbook . . . .   7.50   _____

BOOKS
☐ Kicking Your Stress Habits . . . .   10.00   _____
☐ The Caring Question . . . .   3.95   _____
☐ Philosophical Assumptions . . . .   6.00   _____
☐ Wholistic Health . . . .   12.95   _____
☐ In Our Own Hands . . . .   9.95   _____

TAPES
☐ Daydreams . . . .   9.00   _____
☐ Relax . . . Let Go . . . Relax . . . .   9.00   _____
☐ Spiritual Centering . . . .   9.00   _____
☐ Fingertip Face Massage . . . .   9.00   _____
☐ You Alone Can Be Well . . . But You Can't Be Well Alone! . . .   9.00   _____
☐ Beyond Peptalks and Handouts . . . .   9.00   _____

☐ **THE STRESS KIT** . . . .   29.95   _____
   ☐ StressTalk (cassette workshop) . . . .   15.95   _____
   ☐ PILEUP (educational card game) . . . .   15.95   _____
   ☐ StressRelease (radio program cassette) . . . .   9.95   _____
   ☐ The Stress Examiner (newspaper) . . . .   3.95   _____

SUBTOTAL _____

☐ My check is enclosed (US funds only)

☐ Please charge my bank card
   ☐ VISA   ☐ Mastercard

Card # _____

Expiration date _____

Signature _____

☐ Bill my institution (PO # _____)

Tax (MN residents 6%) _____

*SHIPPING _____

GRAND TOTAL _____

*Shipping. We ship UPS in the US.
Please include $2.50 for the first item
and 50¢ for each additional item. Outside the continental US please add
$4.00.

1 2 3 4 5 6 7 8 9 0 A B C D E F G H I J K L M N O P Q R S T U V W X Y Z